Praise for *Bridges to Health and Healthcare*

"This book is a must-read for those who want to move the health-outcomes needle for the United States. It describes a new way of addressing real-world problems, especially seeing and hearing about healthcare challenges from the vantage point of the person in poverty."

–Shelley White-Means, Executive Director
Consortium on Health Education, Economic
Empowerment, and Research (CHEER), Memphis, TN

"Understanding the impact of poverty on healthcare resource utilization is essential to the achievement of improved quality, lowered cost and improved population health. Bridges to Health and Healthcare *is an important addition to the discipline for hospital administrators, case managers, social workers, nurses, physicians, and anyone caring for patients. In short, this book is for everyone—including the patients themselves—struggling to meet the challenges of healthcare change."*

–George C. Garrow, MD
Medical Director, Hospice/Palliative Care Program,
Oncology and Hematology, Sharon Regional Health
System, Hermitage, PA

"This book creates a rich understanding of why 'obvious' priorities for folks like me who work in public health are not the most 'obvious' priorities or the most salient issues for people in poverty."

–Rev. Kenneth S. Robinson, MD, MDiv
Pastor and Chief Executive, St. Andrew AME Church and
Enterprise; Public Health Policy Adviser, Shelby County
Government; Former Commissioner of Health, State of
Tennessee, Memphis

"Healthcare providers now have a tool for making 'evidence-based' changes within their institutions. This book provides that evidence and gives suggestions to improve patient care and outcomes."

–Nancy E. Garth, BSN, RN, CLNC, FCN
Health Education Coordinator, University of Kentucky
HealthCare-Polk/Dalton Clinic, Lexington, KY

"Bridges to Health and Healthcare offers well-documented approaches and common-sense suggestions. It's a must-read for anyone who seeks to do more than minister to those in poverty, but also to help pull them permanently into prosperity. While written in the context of healthcare, the book can serve as a manual for successful undertakings in all areas of societal improvement."

–The Honorable A. C. Wharton, Jr.
Mayor, City of Memphis, TN

BRIDGES
to Health and Healthcare

New solutions for improving
access and services

Bridges to Health and Healthcare
Payne, Ruby K., Dreussi-Smith, Terie, Shaw, Lucy Y., Young, Jan.
230 pp.
Bibliography pp. 187–194

ISBN: 978-1-938248-34-4

Copyright 2014
Published by aha! Process, Inc.

Copy editing by Dan Shenk and Jesse Conrad
Book design by Paula Nicolella
Cover design by Amy Perich

Printed in the United States of America

The authors gratefully acknowledge permission to reprint charts from the following:

"Paying Wisely: Reforming Incentives to Promote Evidence-Based Decisions at the Point of Care," by E. C. Rich, T. Lake, & C. S. Valenzano (2012). Published by Center on Health Care Effectiveness in collaboration with Mathematica Policy Research.

"The Social Ecology of Health Promotion Interventions," by K. R. McLeroy, A. Steckler, & D. Bibeau (1988). Published in *Health Education Quarterly,* vol. 15, no. 4, pp. 351–377.

BRIDGES
to Health and Healthcare

New solutions for improving
access and services

Ruby K. Payne
Terie Dreussi-Smith
Lucy Y. Shaw
Jan Young

DEDICATION

This book is dedicated to Dr. Rita Pierson, an aha! Process consultant, phenomenal speaker, and extraordinary educator, who died on June 28, 2013. Her spirit, sense of humor, and love of people touched the lives of everyone with whom she came in contact.

Each of us as authors feels so fortunate to have had Rita with us for the time we did. She made our lives immeasurably richer, eased our minds, and laid out the truth in a way that could be absorbed.

As Rita offered her wonderful words that touched so many people so deeply, we hope this book will in turn give you a gift as well—from her through us to you.

ACKNOWLEDGMENTS

A book project of this magnitude—about a subject, health and healthcare, of almost infinite complexity—rests on the sturdy shoulders of more inspiring, helpful, and resourceful individuals than we can count or even identify. But with the acute awareness that we may inadvertently miss naming one or more of our ablest contributors, we nonetheless wish to acknowledge the following persons ...

We begin with special thanks to Kellie Valenti, vice president of Strategic Planning, Ellis Medicine, for making the "business case" for Bridges at Ellis Medicine and within the community of Schenectady, NY.

We appreciate the time and insights of Nicole Baptiste of Ellis Medicine and Dekida Hamler of The Schenectady City Mission for their practical knowledge and insights on how Bridges has been embedded into Ellis protocols.

We want to thank Michael Saccocio of Schenectady Bridges for his support of Ms. Valenti and Ellis Medicine in the institution's major effort to link with the community for the betterment of Ellis Medicine's under-resourced patients.

Further, we extend our gratitude to the very busy and committed members of the healthcare community in Memphis, TN, who generously shared their time and insights: Dr. Reginald Coopwood, president and CEO, The Regional Medical Center at Memphis; Stephen Reynolds, president and CEO, Baptist Healthcare Corporation; Gary Shorb, president and CEO, Methodist Healthcare; Anita Vaughn, administrator and CEO, Baptist Memorial

Hospital for Women; Jamie Patterson, director of Operations, Department of Surgery, University of Tennessee Medical Group; Burt Waller, CEO, Christ Community Health Center; Dr. Peggy Veeser, chair, Department of Nursing, Christian Brothers University; Yvonne Madlock, director, Memphis and Shelby County Health Department; and Elizabeth Bradshaw, family nurse practitioner and healthcare consultant. They were each brilliant in their wisdom and contributions.

Of this group, particular mention is due to two individuals:

Special thanks go to Stephen Reynolds who is retiring after decades of future-oriented thinking in his leadership as president and CEO of the large and successful Baptist Healthcare Corporation of Memphis and surrounding counties. I (Lucy) began my career there and shall be forever grateful for the ways he always allowed me to push the envelope, learn, and grow!

I (Lucy) also am forever indebted to Gary Shorb, CEO of Methodist Healthcare, who lured me away from Baptist Healthcare and prepared me to fill his great big shoes with his shared gifts of encouragement, trust, and profound love of community.

Additional thanks are due to individuals who gave so much to this project; they include:

President and CEO Sherri Rice and Trevor Rice, senior director of Member Services, Access to Healthcare, Reno, NV, provided us with valuable information on how their innovative system uses Bridges in staff training, building relationships of mutual respect, and linking providers with patients who are underinsured and uninsured.

We appreciate Debora McDermed and Cherie Jamason of the Reno, NV, Bridges Out of Poverty Initiative for linking us to Access to Healthcare and for their efforts to bring Bridges concepts and strategies into all sectors and communities in northern Nevada.

We are grateful to Louise Seipel, formerly with The Ohio State University Poverty Solutions Collaborative, who provided us with powerful insights into ways Getting Ahead in a Just-Gettin'-By World graduates were brought into dialogue with healthcare professionals as part of their patient-centered strategic plan—and for her knowledge of how the collaborative used Bridges in community health outreach and other community initiatives.

We thank Nancy Garth and Dr. Linda Alexander, both of the University of Kentucky, Lexington, KY, for being a very valuable team in sharing unique perspectives in ways Bridges to Health and Healthcare has become part of their model in preparing graduate students in the Public Health Department at the University of Kentucky and within the clinical and community health environments in their scope of influence.

We are indebted to Dr. Jane Goleman, Nationwide Children's Hospital, The Ohio State University Department of Medicine, Columbus, OH, for how (over the years) she has provided us with insights into ways she has used Bridges strategies in her practice—and as she prepares medical students for their important work. We acknowledge Dr. Goleman as an early adapter of Bridges to clinical care.

We also are grateful to Michelle Archuleta, Indian Health Services, Bemidji, MN. She has been incredibly creative in working with us in linking the Bridges economic class layer with cultural insights regarding Native Americans—and for her work in folding Bridges into Community Health Coach initiatives.

We wish to acknowledge Maryann Messing, Beaumont Hospital System, Royal Oak, MI, for her behind-the-scenes perspectives on standard interactions between clinical staff with one another, and with patients in one of the most viable hospitals in the Great Lakes region.

With gratitude, in memory of Sister Nardine M. Aquadro, who introduced me (Jan) to the aha! Process body of work.

We acknowledge Philip DeVol as one of the original authors of Bridges Out of Poverty. His ideas have been a significant influence on what Bridges has become; we also thank Phil for his excellent descriptions of mental models for disease and disease management in Chapter 4.

In my own way I (Lucy) wish to acknowledge Dr. Rita Pierson who first introduced me to a live presentation of "Bridges." I watched her, was led to alternating fits of tears and laughter, and knew in those moments that I wanted to bring this work to the world of health and healthcare. And my dear friend Jan Young, a co-author of this book, saw to it that I got the privilege to do so.

And I (Lucy) offer special thanks to co-author Terie Dreussi-Smith, for tilling the field of healthcare, and to our beloved co-author Ruby Payne, for her deep wisdom and sacrifice as she continues to go where others fear to tread.

We extend great thanks to our publishing team—Peggy Conrad, Dan Shenk, Jesse Conrad, and Paula Nicolella—for their exceptional wisdom, skill, and gentle "nudgings."

And finally, thank you for reading our book. The authors have found that working together has brought us strong synergy—and even a little serendipity—as we merged our perspectives into one. We hope you find the same energy as you read and use *Bridges to Health and Healthcare.*

TABLE OF CONTENTS

PREFACE

In 1996 I wrote the book *A Framework for Understanding Poverty* to help educators who were dealing with students from poverty. The book basically articulated and named the reality of generational poverty or, as the federal government calls it, "persistent poverty." It was based on 30 years of experience living close to poverty in Haiti (for 3½ months) and in the United States. My former husband, Frank (deceased in 2010), had grown up in poverty and, during the marriage, I learned a great deal about both situational and generational poverty from him and his extended family. I had no idea that my 30-year longitudinal study would go on to impact so many other disciplines and fields of study.

In the ensuing years, the information in *A Framework for Understanding Poverty* was applied to schools and then social work and then community development. It went on to be used by businesses, churches and other religious organizations, judicial systems, first responders, correctional facilities, and law enforcement. It is now used in a number of countries around the world.

A few years later Philip E. DeVol, Terie Dreussi-Smith and I wrote a book called *Bridges Out of Poverty: Strategies for Professionals and Communities.* The book incorporated many of the concepts of Framework and also described practical ways that individuals, institutions, and communities could work systemically and individually to make changes in relation to poverty.

Since then, more than 200 "Bridges Communities" have been established in the U.S. and other countries. These communities take proactive steps in addressing issues of poverty, including the engagement of individuals who have been in generational poverty in the process of making changes at all levels.

This book, *Bridges to Health and Healthcare,* is the application of the understandings about generational poverty and Bridges strategies to the healthcare field. A disparity in healthcare outcomes for individuals in poverty compared with other socioeconomic classes clearly exists—throughout the world. As one of our authors, Jan Young, an RN with a doctorate in nursing, states, "I have discovered that most healthcare delivery outcomes that are undesirable can be traced to a resource or communication issue."

The *daily reality* of generational poverty is minimally understood by most institutions and practitioners because it often isn't articulated in a way that can be comprehended, even by well-educated individuals. Policy and law tend to be made by individuals far removed from the reality of generational poverty. And each entity—at the individual level, at the institutional level, and at the community level—has its own purposes and needs. This book identifies many of the underlying layers that prevent the desired health outcomes.

Furthermore, Western countries tend to see socioeconomic class in terms of one resource: money. This book will introduce the concept of class as a set of nine resources. The stability or instability of resources impact health outcomes significantly.

The three lenses of individual, institutional, and community (sometimes called the Bridges triple lens) will be used to examine the layering effect of unstable resources as they come in contact with institutional and community structures and the consequent impact on health and healthcare outcomes.

Additionally, we are adding two research bases to the current discussion on healthcare outcomes: efficacy—at the individual, institutional, and community level—and communication. Efficacy is usually a missing component of the discussion in health outcomes, as are the underlying, often missed communication issues.

Our fivefold call to action is this:

1. Read the book.

2. Examine your own practices in light of this information.

3. Identify the steps you will take to implement this information into your own practice.

4. Contact us for discussion: (800) 424-9484.

5. Allow us to help you implement it.

To your health—and the health of those you work with.

Ruby K. Payne, PhD
for
Terie Dreussi-Smith, MAEd
Lucy Y. Shaw, MBA
Jan Young, DNSc

INTRODUCTION

Health status is defined by the World Health Organization as "a state of complete physical, mental, and social well-being and not merely the absence of disease or infirmity."[1] A study sponsored by the National Institutes of Health reported in January 2012 that "compared to 17 high-income countries, the United States is at or near the bottom in at least nine indicators."[2] Included in that list of indicators are infant mortality, heart and lung disease, sexually transmitted infections, and adolescent pregnancies. The list also includes the more systemic issues, such as injuries, homicides, and rates of disability.

What is clearly understood (please also see the research in Chapter 2 and in Appendix C) is the following:

- Costs of health and healthcare are increasing annually in the United States. Each year the "bite" out of the government budget grows.

- The numbers and percentage of individuals who are obese continues to increase.

- The majority of baby boomers are going to be on Medicare by 2020. As one ages, healthcare costs usually increase.

- Health is directly related to education and socioeconomic status.

    The better educated you are, the healthier you are. According to Moss, socioeconomic factors that affect impoverished populations such as education, income inequality, and occupation represent the strongest and most consistent predictors of health and mortality … Education is a major social determinant of health, with educational attainment related to improved health outcomes, due to its effect on income, employment and living conditions.[3]

    Degrees of social status are closely linked to health inequalities. Those with poor health tend to fall into poverty, and the poor tend to have poor health. According to the World Health Organization, within countries those of lower socioeconomic strata have the worst health outcomes. Health also appears to have a strong social component linking it to education and access to information. In terms of health, poverty includes low income, low education, social exclusion and environmental decay. The poor within most countries are trapped in a cycle in which poverty breeds ill health and ill health breeds poverty.[4]

The greater the level of being under-resourced, the less effective our institutions and governments are in achieving better outcomes. The following outcomes are inextricably linked to poverty:

- The average age of death is younger in poverty.
- Primary care is often the emergency room.
- Dental visits are fewer.
- Obesity and diabetes rates are higher.
- The rates of amount of cigarette smoking is higher.
- Access to medical care is less.
- The allostatic load (physiological response of the body to repeated or chronic stress) created by poverty literally lowers IQ.[5] (Also see Appendix C.)

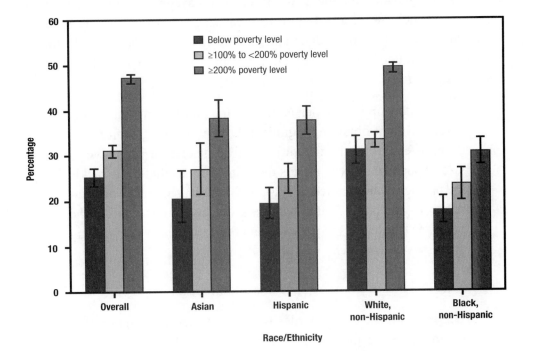

Percentage of Adults Who Reported Excellent or Very Good Health by Income and Race—May 31, 2013

Source: Summary Health Statistics for the U.S. Population:
National Health Interview Survey, 2011.

IT'S NOT ABOUT LACK OF ENERGY OR EFFORT

Those working in the healthcare industry, as well as consumers and others, are all searching for answers to the kinds of questions and issues raised above—answers that will have far-reaching impact on the physical, financial, and intellectual capacity of our nation. It is analogous to the search for the mythical Holy Grail as spectacularly filmed in "Indiana Jones and the Last Crusade."

We believe we are all in a real-life epic adventure in pursuit of the healthcare equivalent of the Holy Grail: a multifaceted solution to a huge, complex, and expensive problem. Every day, courageous caregivers step out in sheer faith and courage in an attempt to provide ethical, effective, and respectful care to the growing numbers of people moving in and out of the system. It is for these individuals—and for all of us charged with finding bridges to the Holy Grail of healthcare delivery—that we write this book.

When we look at the huge number of initiatives for change and the dollars spent on lobbying for legislative change, innovations in medical research, sophisticated diagnostic, treatment, and information systems, professional training, and so much more, any failure to create a system that produces better health outcomes could not be due to lack of effort! Edwin Friedman, the rabbi, psychologist, leadership guru, and author in his last great work, *A Failure of Nerve: Leadership in the Age of the Quick Fix,* says:

> … [L]eadership in America is stuck in the rut of trying harder and harder without obtaining significantly new results. The rut runs deep, affecting all the institutions of our society irrespective of size or purpose. It even affects those institutions that try to tackle the problem: universities, think-tanks, and consultants. These institutions are "stuck," and there exists a connection between the paralysis that leaders experience and the paralysis in the thinking processes of those who would get them unstuck.[6]

Magnifying this line of thinking, Friedman continues:

> The treadmill of trying harder is driven by the assumption that failure is due to the fact that one did not try hard enough, use the right technique, or get enough information. This assumption overlooks the possibility that thinking processes themselves are stuck and imagination gridlocked, not because of cognitive strictures in the minds of those trying to solve a problem, but because of emotional processes within the wider relationship system. The failure to recognize those emotional processes, if not the outright denial of their existence, is what often initiates and ultimately perpetuates the treadmill effect.[7]

When we look at health legislation of the past three decades, we see policies that "disincentivize" creativity that was directed at better ways to create optimal, sustainable population health. Instead we see rules and regulations designed to curb the flow of rising costs that too often actually create more expenses for all parties. These are responded to by institutions with solutions that are often restrictive and competitive while focused on maximizing reimbursement. We do not presume to propose the eradication of this business model. We simply wish to offer alternative models for addressing what has brought us to the edge of the abyss.

Furthermore, in the maze of legislation, attempts, and rhetoric to make health-care more available to the poor, the disparities in health outcomes by poverty and race continue to grow as the gap between rich and poor in this country continues to widen.

The focus in much of institutional healthcare tends to be on treating patients in a nondiscriminatory manner. Perhaps in some instances, however, patients *should* be treated differently because they *are* different. Poverty certainly creates different lenses through which to view and manage life and health.

THE PLAN FOR THIS BOOK

Collectively, the co-authors of this book represent some 120 years of experience in education and healthcare leadership and participation. Two of the authors of this book are healthcare careerists with vast exposure to changes dubbed as "reform" initiated by the government, by researchers, and by healthcare professionals over the past 30 years. Some have created positive change, and some have not. This book is not about addressing the rightness or wrongness of the Patient Protection and Affordable Care Act (ACA) of 2010. It is intended to add what we believe to be a necessary lens for effective change.

Do we dare to suggest that our model, *Bridges to Health and Heathcare,* is the only solution for you, the reader? No, of course we don't. But we do believe that you will find our model elegantly practical in its construct, assumptions, and application.

All we ask is that, in the spirit of Indiana Jones and his search for the Holy Grail, you put our ideas to the test by taking a leap of faith and courage as together we seek a sturdy bridge to efficacious healthcare delivery.

> **This book is not about addressing the rightness or wrongness of the Patient Protection and Affordable Care Act (ACA) of 2010. It is intended to add what we believe to be a necessary lens for effective change.**

And yes, as with our hero Indy, the uncertainty posed by recent legislation and other onrushing developments can create fear, anger, and ego conflict, all of which are intrinsic to great challenges! We hope you will consider the possibilities and join with us in finding ways to adopt these ideas.

PART I: APPROACHING THE BRIDGE

CHAPTER ONE

THE 'BRIDGES' LENS AND TWO CASE STUDIES

As noted in the Preface, this book is based on "Bridges" concepts and constructs. They are foundational to *Bridges to Health and Healthcare* and include the following:

- **Bridges is not a program but a lens.**

  The Bridges lens is used in healthcare, education, law enforcement, and other sectors to accurately define economic class environments.

- **It is important to use accurate mental models.**

  Base plans on accurate mental models of poverty, middle class, and wealth. Interventions don't usually work very well when the models are inaccurate.

- **Define class as a set of resources.**

  Bridges identifies poverty and wealth in terms of nine resources: financial, emotional (mental health and coping strategies), mental (as it relates to cognition), spiritual, physical, support systems (positive social capital), relationships/role models, knowledge of hidden rules (unspoken cues, norms, and expectations), and language/communication. The fewer of these nine resources you have, the more under-resourced you are. To be under-resourced is often to be in a "survival" environment. When resources are stable (i.e., you know where you will sleep at night, that you will have food, etc.) it's possible to plan. We refer to generally stable environments as "middle class." The more resources you have, the greater your ability to make choices. We refer to abundantly resourced environments as "wealth."

- **Hidden rules result from environmental demands and learned responses.**

When a person has been in a survival environment or a stable environment or a wealthy environment for at least two generations, there is a shared understanding (a collective efficacy) of how the world works and the "hidden rules" that govern it. These hidden rules exist by race, by religion, by region of the country, by socioeconomic class. They become an issue when the environment changes or when there is bridging social capital (getting to know someone different from you).

- **"Stable environment" rules and stable resources have an impact on planning and change.**

Most institutions tend to use "stable environment" rules to operate and assume that all clients and patients are using those rules *and* are understanding those rules. If a client or patient does not use those rules, then the institution tends to believe that the person is either rude or stupid. Many institutions create interventions that assume a set of stable resources is available to the client.

> **Most institutions tend to use "stable environment" rules to operate and assume that all clients and patients are using those rules *and* are understanding those rules.**

- **Relationships of mutual respect are essential and lead to inclusiveness in decision making.**

A community or institution cannot have policies, procedures, and interventions that actually work unless they have all three socioeconomic classes at the decision-making table. All learning is double-coded both emotionally and cognitively.[8] The emotional coding is done through relationships.

- **Under-resourced adults are problem solvers.**

  Most adults in under-resourced environments have tremendous strengths and are problem solvers, but they may not have the underlying resources, knowledge, or capacity to participate in most institutions as expected or required. If an individual is seen as being needy or deficient, that perception is often reflected in the communication and approach to efficacy.

- **Knowledge is a key form of privilege and is related to how you spend your time.**

  How a person spends his/her time determines the knowledge bases he/she accesses.

- **All causes of poverty and all research bases must be used to create solutions.**

  When solutions are sought for an institution, all four causes of poverty and all six research bases for healthcare must be taken into account in order to arrive at workable solutions. To use only one or two causes or research bases is to create solutions that ultimately are not viable.

- **Patterns, not stereotypes, are used.**

  The patterns identified by environment are simply that—patterns. The brain sorts in patterns. This doesn't mean, however, that everyone in that environment uses those patterns. Stereotypes occur when the patterns of a group are applied to everyone in the group. If that is done with this work, then the information would be misused and not helpful.

- **How one survives in poverty is very different from how one survives in school, work, and institutions.**

  To survive in poverty, one must be non-verbal, sensory, and reactive. To survive in school, work, or an institution requires one to be verbal, to use abstract/representational systems, and to be proactive. Many of these are learned in formative environments.

- **Three issues are pivotal in making transitions.**

  The three principal factors that help you make the transition to a more resourced life are education, employment, and bridging social capital (people who are different from you). Money gets you past survival, but it does not change your thinking.

- **Community and institutional resources make a huge difference in individual resources and efficacy.**

  Community resources make a big difference for individuals and influence the stability of communities. When there is little dialogue between the resourced and under-resourced, communities have more individuals living in unstable situations. Plans must be based on the premise that people of all classes, sectors, and political persuasions are problem solvers and need to be at the decision-making table.

- **Emphasize working together to build sustainable communities.**

  The goal is to build economically sustainable communities in which everyone can live well.

HOW THE BRIDGES LENS CAN MAKE A PRACTICAL DIFFERENCE

The Bridges lens is a tool that can counteract natural tendencies to judge. As the next story illustrates, it is helpful to examine our assumptions and perceptions.

Those familiar with the work of Stephen R. Covey may remember the story (from *7 Habits of Highly Effective People*) about the man on the train.

> *I remember one Sunday morning, on a subway in New York; people were sitting quietly—some reading, some lost in thought, some resting or sleeping—then suddenly, a man and his children entered the subway car. The children were so loud that instantly, the whole climate changed. The man sat down next to me and closed his eyes, apparently neglecting the situation. The children were yelling back and forth, throwing things; it was very disturbing, and yet the man sitting next to me did nothing.*
>
> *I could not believe that he could be so insensitive as to leave his children like that and doing nothing about it. So finally, with unusual patience, I turned to him and said, "Sir, your children are really disturbing a lot of people. I wonder if you couldn't control them a little more." The man lifted his gaze as if to come to consciousness of the situation for the first time and said softly, "Oh, you're right, I guess I should do something about it; we just came*

from the hospital where their mother died about an hour ago. I don't know what to do, and I guess they don't know how to handle it either."

At that moment, my paradigm shifted. Suddenly I saw things differently, behaved differently; my irritation vanished. I didn't have to worry about my attitude or my behavior; my heart was filled with the man's pain. Feelings of sympathy and compassion flowed freely. "Your wife has just died? Oh, I'm sorry! Can you tell me about it? What can I do to help?" Everything changed in an instant.[9]

With more information, the man engaged in a totally different way with the father of the children. Throughout this book, we offer for your consideration the premise that getting a little more information and developing relationships of mutual respect and trust may make a significant difference in outcomes with patients.

There are many wonderful programs for individuals, institutions, and communities. Often, after significant financial investment, we find that people are struggling to understand why the latest great program did not work. Perhaps, at the very basic level, they failed or did not achieve the optimal results because of something as simple as the lenses through which the people implementing those wonderful programs saw the world. Those lenses—so skillfully polished by beliefs, environment, tradition, culture, family history, and experiences—affect both our conscious and subconscious perspectives and behaviors.

We offer the tools in this book as one set of glasses for those lenses. Try them on. Perhaps you will find that they require further refinement or polishing from the wealth of your own knowledge and experiences. We welcome that.

> **Those lenses—so skillfully polished by beliefs, environment, tradition, culture, family history, and experiences—affect both our conscious and subconscious perspectives and behaviors.**

QUESTIONS FOR REFLECTION

1. What are some clues that a mental model might not be accurate?

2. Are there "hidden rules" for your work group or practice setting? About work assignments or certain work schedules? Do you belong to any organizations with "hidden rules"? What happens when someone breaks a "hidden rule"?

3. Give an example of a pattern. How does that differ from a stereotype?

4. Have you ever experienced an incident like encountering the man on the train? If so, think about the experience of initially misreading a situation. How did you feel when you did that?

The following two case studies are intended to help the reader use the Bridges lens to analyze real-life examples of healthcare in action (or inaction). A set of questions follows both studies, and each is debriefed. These case studies also are designed for discussion.

The first case study illustrates how the healthcare system functioned for an individual from the upper middle class. The second shows how an individual from poverty interacted with institutional healthcare—and vice versa.

CASE STUDY #1—FRANCIS AND ELIZABETH

Francis and Elizabeth Rossi are an upper-middle-class couple who have been married for many years with three adult children. Francis is retired from a high-level management position at a major U.S. defense corporation. He has a doctorate in aeronautical engineering. Elizabeth is a retired first-grade teacher who spent a number of years as a stay-at-home mom and also a good deal of time as a caretaker for her aging parents. Elizabeth grew up in the middle class; her father had a degree in business and was a successful small-business owner and farmer. Francis's father had no education beyond eighth grade and worked in a factory. Francis is the only person in his large extended family who has a PhD. His parents couldn't contribute very much to his higher education.

Both Elizabeth and Francis have wonderful relationships with their children, as well as a large group of friends who are also upper-middle-class professionals. They both have contact with their siblings, but only one of their siblings is considered to be a "part of their family" at this point. This person is also someone who has achieved some level of professional success. Elizabeth and Francis, both of whom are retired, live in the mid-South close to one of their married children—and have a great relationship with their grandchildren as well. In the summers in recent years, they have enjoyed living aboard their 42-foot trawler powerboat in a resort area with ocean access. They typically live aboard from May until October. Many of their couple friends are also "live aboards."

Francis and Elizabeth just got onto Medicare, with the supplemental insurance included as part of his retirement package. They also have some solid financial assets in addition to their retirement benefits.

One day when Elizabeth was shopping with a friend, she called Francis who was on the boat. At first he didn't answer; she called multiple times. When she finally got through to him, he was slurring his words, told her he had a bad headache, and was throwing up a lot. He had suffered headaches off and on for a week, which was unusual. So Elizabeth suspected that something was seriously wrong, probably a stroke. So from her car she called 911, as well as the harbor master, asking him to go down to be with Francis until she and the ambulance arrived. Francis was taken to the local hospital's emergency room, and a life flight was available to airlift him to a major trauma center 70 miles away.

Elizabeth says they were very fortunate that they were close to this particular trauma center, which has an entire floor dedicated to brain aneurisms and injuries. Francis was diagnosed with a subarachnoid hemorrhage (spider-like veins had burst in the brain stem). The good news was that the bleeding stopped on its own. However, the prognosis was very poor. Forty to fifty percent of people with this condition die immediately, most of the rest have some disability, and only 10% survive with full recovery and little brain damage. Francis was like a baby—he couldn't even walk. He was admitted and was in the intensive-care unit for six weeks, then had a short stay on the regular floor, with three more weeks of inpatient rehabilitation.

During this time, Francis had multiple complications. His brain swelled, and he had vasospasms, which resulted in a frontal-lobe stroke. He also developed severe pneumonia, high fevers of up to 106, and some heart problems. He had to be catheterized and was very much like an infant physically, though some cognitive functioning was returning. He couldn't move around in case he would jostle something in his brain. At one point his catheter tube got stopped up. Francis sensed something was wrong and was able to communicate to the nurse. His capacity to speak was very limited. He would have to be sedated to get his scans because it was very hard for him to stay still. He was almost totally dependent. He couldn't remember most past life events. Once he looked up at Elizabeth and asked, "Does my mother know about this?" Elizabeth had to tell him his mother had been deceased for eight years.

The day Francis was admitted, one of their boating-couple friends who had heard what was happening found Elizabeth at the small-town ER and offered to drive her the 70 miles to the hospital in the city. Another couple happened to call, saying "Hey, we're in town." They were in the city where Francis was being transported. Elizabeth asked them to go to the hospital to be with Francis until she could get there. And yet another couple who had just flown in from Houston called to let them know they were in town on business. This couple also immediately went to the trauma center to support Elizabeth and Francis.

Elizabeth checked in to a hotel that catered to the trauma center—with shuttle service. The hotel bill for more than two months was nearly $2,500, and her food expenses were at least another $500. Their son flew up from the mid-South to be with them for three weeks; he owned his own software company and could work from anywhere. When you take into consideration all of the family airfares, room, board and food, and hospital bills, the bill exceeded $20,000 out of their pocket to give Francis the support he needed.

Elizabeth had experience working with physicians and healthcare providers when she was the primary caregiver for her parents. In her words, Elizabeth's view could be summed up as follows:

> You have to think of everything when you have a loved one inpatient. You have to be there for doctor rounds, you must understand who the powerful physicians are and the questions to ask. If you have someone with you all day and evening with your inpatient loved one, the care will be better. You must fend for that person, especially if they are incapacitated or elderly. You force yourself to ask that powerful doctor a question he/she may think is dumb. You appear cheerful to everyone, including the patient.

One physician was frustrated with Elizabeth's seemingly endless questions. But she says most of them "were helpful and nice." Elizabeth would not allow herself to stop advocating or asking questions or be intimidated—for Francis. Elizabeth believes the fact that Francis had a doctorate enabled him to get a bit more attention from the clinical staff, as well as enhanced her ability to negotiate for him. The nurses helped her create a photoboard for "Dr. Francis" (Dr. Francis loves boating, Jack Daniels, his grandchildren, etc.); it made him more human to his caregivers when he was lying there practically in a coma. Elizabeth says a side benefit of the photoboard was that it helped Francis remember who he was!

Elizabeth viewed herself as an advocate, but in this case the prognosis was so critical that she got more information from the staff than most patient advocates. But she still asked physicians and nurses multiple questions—and she was looking at all the information about vasospasms and arachnoid bleeds online just about every night at the hotel. There were a few physician friends whom Elizabeth also would call occasionally for advice. Some of the more engaging nurses gave Elizabeth information on what key milestones and benchmarks to look for in brain-trauma recovery.

Elizabeth had to go to the hospital on the shuttle. She had to make sure she got sleep and eat a little. She had two beers most nights but never overindulged; she always had to be in control. Safety was a big concern both at the trauma center and later riding the city bus from the hotel to the rehab hospital. The rehab hospital, they were told, was a better place for people of their "status" than the rehab at the trauma center hospital. At the trauma hospital, less fortunate families had to sleep in the waiting room because they couldn't afford a hotel.

One night there was a violent incident between two families in the ER over a fatal gang shooting. The entire center went on lockdown. It irritated Elizabeth that gang-related brain-trauma patients would get triage precedence over Francis, a man who had worked hard all his life and had made his contribution to society. She felt bad for the family who had lost a loved one, but she felt it was wrong for her husband to have his care affected because someone else was into drugs and violence. She was worried for their safety. "Here's a hospital on prime ocean-view property in a neighborhood where it's unsafe to even walk around," she told a friend.

Francis eventually recovered completely, with most of his cognitive capacity intact. He learned how to compensate for the brain deficits he suffered. And he was able to once again captain his boat in open waters each summer and return to his former quality of life.

QUESTIONS

1. What were the resources of these individuals? Using a scale of 1–3 (1 is under-resourced, 2 is stable resources, and 3 is abundant resources), rate the resources of both individuals.

Resource	Elizabeth	Francis
Financial		
Emotional		
Mental/cognitive		
Spiritual (future story)		
Physical		
Support systems		
Relationships/role models		
Knowledge of hidden rules		
Language/formal register		

2. Which of these research bases most impacted the healthcare delivery outcomes? Why?

Access	Availability	Cost	Quality	Efficacy	Communication

3. What could have been done differently to enhance the outcomes?

ADDITIONAL QUESTIONS AND DEBRIEFING

1. The patient in a coma was someone who was a high-achieving individual with considerable cognitive capacity. Beyond issues of insurance and access to healthcare, how might Francis's career and pedigree have made a difference in how the clinical staff perceived and prioritized Francis?

2. Which of the nine resources might be missing if Francis and Elizabeth were living in generational poverty? Francis and Elizabeth had experienced a high-level quality of life for multiple decades. How do you think this quality-of-life experience impacted Elizabeth's motivation to do everything in her power to get Francis back to wellness?

3. Elizabeth was very persistent in her efforts at the hospital. With only a few bumps on the road, she was able to navigate the healthcare system at the trauma center for more than two months. If she were a woman in generational poverty with a husband with brain trauma, to what extent might Elizabeth's strategies have appeared to be "manipulation" rather than "negotiation"? Why?

INSTITUTIONAL CASE STUDY

CASE STUDY #2—CLINIC READMISSIONS: BILL

Approximately 30 years ago in a particular government hospital in a large urban center, a recently assigned nurse practitioner to the Ambulatory Care Clinic made an observation. There appeared to be a group of patients who routinely had to be readmitted to the clinic about every four months.

This seemed peculiar. On reviewing the records of not only that group of patients assigned to her but also to other providers, the pattern seemed to be consistent. For example, the patient presented with hypertension (high blood pressure), hyperglycemia (high blood sugar), or usually both. The patient would be followed in the clinic for multiple visits, sometimes over several months; provided medications during that period; often referred to the nutritionist or diabetes educator or social worker for other issues; have follow-up visits; be stabilized on his/her medication regimen; and then discharged from the clinic with very detailed instructions.

For the visits prior to discharge, transportation costs were reimbursed to the patient. At the time of discharge, the patient would be provided with 90 days' worth of medication, a prescription, and four refills to cover the time before the next scheduled appointment. Depending on the patient's eligibility for benefits, the costs for refilling the prescriptions would be paid by the patient. Travel costs to any subsequent visits were not reimbursed (some lived in outlying rural communities).

In checking the records of these particular patients in this group, the nurse practitioner found that they typically presented to the emergency room in crisis. This usually resulted in readmission to the hospital, followed by a subsequent discharge to the Ambulatory Care Clinic. At the time of discharge, someone had typically documented that the patient "verbalized and demonstrated understanding of his/her instructions."

When she would ask the patients in the group about what happened, they would tell her different reasons, but the common response was that they had stopped taking their medications and they hadn't refilled their prescriptions. The pharmacist said they were "noncompliant."

One of these patients was Bill Johnson. Bill came to the emergency room one evening with elevated blood pressure, an extremely high blood-glucose level, and a stasis ulcer on his heel. When the ER staff did the history and physical assessment, Bill admitted he hadn't been taking his meds. The notation on the chart was that patient was noncompliant. He was admitted to the floor. He was assigned to an attending physician who was in charge of a new set of interns and residents. Those interns and residents had been taught particular protocols. Those protocols were associated with specific diagnoses and clinical pathways. Billing clerks were assigned the responsibility of assuring that all coding was correct to maximize the highest amount of payment.

Bill was well-known to the nursing staff. The attending physician, however, was new to Bill, who seemed to take some delight in withholding key bits of information from interns and residents, knowing it would create frenzied activity during rounds. He knew the routine and could have conducted the rounds himself if he wanted to. They usually asked the same questions, and he could tell which interns were better prepared than others. This time a wound-care team was assigned to him for the treatment of his stasis ulcer. By now, he knew when he saw the utilization review nurse looking at his chart, he could pretty much count the days before he was discharged to the clinic. They had run the usual tests, and he had basically been stabilized.

Bill was, as he predicted, discharged to the clinic. There he reconnected with a familiar face, the nurse practitioner assigned to his care. He felt comfortable in the clinic around the people there, most of whom knew him and addressed him by name. He didn't like going to the nutritionist and the diabetes patient educator because he already knew "that stuff." They told him it was policy, and he needed to go.

When discussing with the nurse practitioner (who asked him what was really going on with him, noting his pattern of readmissions) the risks involved in noncompliance with his medication regimen, Bill replied, "Meds cost too much. Why can't they just give them to me?"

QUESTIONS

1. Which of these research bases most impacted the healthcare delivery outcomes? Why?

2. What could have been done differently to enhance the outcomes?

Access	Availability	Cost	Quality	Efficacy	Communication

QUESTIONS AND DEBRIEFING

1. From the perspective of the institution, what actions could have been taken? What incentives may have contributed to unintended consequences?

2. What did Bill seem to understand about the financial aspects of the situation that the healthcare professionals may have been missing?

3. In reviewing these readmissions, what were the costs of the admissions and subsequent care compared with the costs of prescriptions?

4. Did the payments made to the hospital for caring for patients during these cycles of readmissions to the hospital and clinic justify ignoring the pattern in this isolated group of patients?

5. How might future policies about readmissions within a certain time frame affect the hospital's attention to the pattern observed by the nurse practitioner?

6. If this were happening today—given penalties for reimbursements— what institutional policies might change?

The Bridges lens also can be used to analyze four more case studies that appear in Chapter 7.

CHAPTER TWO

OVERVIEW OF THE RESEARCH INTO HEALTH AND HEALTHCARE

Attempting to understand all the variables that influence and affect health-care and decision making is as complex as attempting to unravel a spider's web without breaking the strands. With our minds spinning with all the "what ifs" and "yes, buts," we take a step back to recall how all this evolved.

Twenty years ago the dialogue about health and healthcare revolved around what was called the "three-legged stool"—*access, availability,* and *cost.* Later, *quality* was added as an important and progressive adjunct to the list. In the *Bridges to Health and Healthcare* model, we are adding *efficacy* and *communication* as meaningful attributes that the industry now finds itself working hard to address in an environment of threats to both financial resources and image.

Health and healthcare disparities research also is a key piece of the puzzle. Analysis of that follows later in this chapter.

The six research bases are outlined—with examples—in the following chart. After the chart are descriptions and further explanation regarding each of the six categories.

HEALTHCARE RESEARCH BASES

ACCESS	AVAILABILITY	COST
DEFINITION: Ability to enter or engage healthcare provider, system, or resource	**DEFINITION:** The conditions and time frame in which care can be received or allowed	**DEFINITION:** For services offered or provided—actual fees, price charged, amount paid—profitability
EXAMPLES: Public transportation Insurance—types Insurance—co-pay Providers—types, numbers, and locations Appointment process Provider/agency policies Contact information Medication—types	**EXAMPLES:** Specialty care options Providers—types, numbers, mix Hours of operation Locations of providers Continuity of care Fragmentation in delivery system Case management Referral system Policies—regulatory legislation Competition between and among providers Ideology around certain populations (e.g., prisoners) Knowledge of system Medication use Transportation	**EXAMPLES:** Payer source Insurance Reimbursement models Types of medication and cost Billing processes Coding Legal/regulatory requirements Paperwork costs Preventive care Non-coverage of complementary and alternative medicine Different pricing of over-the-counter meds based on neighborhood Time payment Policies Cost of readmissions

ACCESS

One only needs to do a simple exercise about economic class to determine the types of healthcare services available in various neighborhoods. Have you ever seen a plastic surgeon's office in the "'hood"? What kind of access do people from the various economic classes have to certain types of providers, for example, a world-class specialist for a non-emergency consultation? What's the

QUALITY	EFFICACY	COMMUNICATION
DEFINITION: The extent to which services provided actually improve health outcomes	**DEFINITION:** Capacity to produce desired or optimal health outcome at individual, institutional, community, and policy level	**DEFINITION:** Verbal and non-verbal tools for reciprocal shared meaning and messages that positively impact health outcomes
EXAMPLES: Standards of practice Sub-optimal management plans Knowledge of system Level of continuity of delivery system Level of fragmentation of delivery system Knowledge bases and experience of providers' staffs Competition among health systems Wraparound case management services Appropriate materials and explanations Trauma treatment	**EXAMPLES:** Individual resource analysis (9 resources— financial, emotional, mental, spiritual, physical, support systems, relationships/ role models, knowledge of hidden rules, formal register) Community resource analysis Outcomes and disparities by subgroup (race, class, gender) Social cohesion (having everyone represented at table) Social coherence (does this make sense?) Patient compliance Readmissions Change models	**EXAMPLES:** Hidden rules Formal register Abstract representational systems Impact of poverty on planning, thinking, and allostatic load. Information gathering from story—plot versus character info Mental models for communication Role of one-on-one relationships in compliance Role of non-verbals in survival environment Role of "voice" in change

Source: R. K. Payne & J. Young.

perceived quality of care at a free clinic? How many people from wealth or even middle class might we see standing in line for care at a free clinic? What kind of care do we think we can afford depending on our economic class? Can we afford over-the-counter drugs? If we can get transportation and pay for the visit, can we afford to fill the prescription?

AVAILABILITY

Many of us have observed—and experienced—the unintended consequences of well-intended interventions to "help" the poor. An intervention that directly affects access to healthcare in some communities is the movement of households in poverty to mixed-income neighborhoods. If geography alone were a cure for poverty, that could have been accomplished many years ago. Without the social cohesion and assimilation between groups in these neighborhoods, little except the change of the appearance in the physical space is achieved.

In some cases the lack of a robust public transportation system and limited access to providers who will "accept" these relocated families for non-urgent care presents a new challenge. One of the common stories from ambulance services is the number of individuals from poverty who call the ambulance to go to the emergency room because they don't have transportation, not because the health issue is life-threatening. Furthermore, what hours is the clinic open? What is the cost to the clinic to stay open for 24 hours? How do you get to the clinic in rural areas?

COST

Data and research have explored healthcare costs from multiple perspectives. Many seem to agree that there are multiple drivers of healthcare costs, including an aging population, unhealthy lifestyles, costs of medications, and the cost of chronic care disease management. Overspending in the health system has been calculated at up to $1.2 trillion of the $2.2 trillion spent in the United States. Plunkett Research projects that healthcare costs in the U.S. will hit $3.5 trillion by 2016.[10] More than half of all health spending occurs in two areas: (1) "defensive medicine," which is linked to excessive tests and treatment driven largely by concerns over litigation, and (2) inefficiency and the cost of care necessitated by such conditions as obesity and other lifestyle-related preventable diseases.

In September 2013 the Henry J. Kaiser Family Foundation published a report on the 47 million non-elderly Americans who were uninsured as of 2012. "Going without coverage can have serious health consequences for the uninsured because they receive less preventive care, and delayed care often results in more serious illness requiring advanced treatment," typically resulting in higher costs.[11]

This underscores the importance of placing costs as an equal "leg of the stool" for *Bridges to Health and Healthcare.* Healthcare institutions and providers (for-profits and not-for-profits, safety-net hospitals and non-safety-net hospitals) are under increasing scrutiny, which is leading to enhanced innovation. Most providers are looking for cost-neutral approaches to maintain and improve quality of care.

In addition to individual costs, there are of course institutional costs. One county hospital system had a huge problem with the control of morphine supplies; the annual 12-month supply was gone in five months. Institutional costs also include unfunded emergency room visits and hospital readmissions, personnel turnover, equipment, competition for specialized physicians, and treatment of the uninsured.

Then there are community costs to county and city governments: medical transportation (helicopters, underfunded ambulance services, etc.) and unexpected healthcare expenses due to natural disasters (hurricanes, blizzards, tornadoes, floods, etc.). All of these cost issues erode profitability, as well as health outcomes.

A few years ago Kellie Valenti, vice president of Strategic Planning and Program Development at Ellis Medicine, Schenectady, NY, presented the "business case" for using the Bridges lens, tracking how the model would positively impact the Ellis emergency department and unreimbursed readmissions. "Bridges is not just another thing," she said recently. "Bridges is important at every level within our organization—and not just for the direct caregivers. Bridges has offered Ellis fiscal sustainability that is budget-neutral: It's an easy sell." For more about the Ellis story, please see Chapter 5. And for more on cost-related research, see Appendix C.

QUALITY

Are health and healthcare rights or privileges? How one answers that question directly influences perceptions about quality. Many times perception of quality parallels perception of options. Although economic class does not equate to options and perceptions of them, it certainly influences them.

> **Are health and healthcare rights or privileges?**

Safety-net hospitals, for example, are frequently viewed as the primary destination for the poor and uninsured who become ill or have a personal injury. While middle-class and wealthy individuals might occasionally choose to go to a safety-net hospital in the event of trauma, most commercially insured patients usually opt to go elsewhere. Despite the ability of most safety-net hospitals to meet or exceed the accreditation standards of the U.S.-based Joint Commission and despite the large number of board-certified specialty providers at these hospitals, they are frequently seen as a less desirable option for medical care—with the exception of trauma.

Disparities and perceptions of quality also show up in settings where care is provided with a limited formulary of drugs. The quantity and perceived "quality" of the medications may be called into question by those who believe that access to non-generic options may be better, even when that may not actually be accurate or true.

Although there are certain gaps in the research, studies assessing physician perception of clients based on race and socioeconomics are available for review. Those perceptions, one can argue, affect behavior, thus relationship, ultimately influencing both perception of quality and actual quality of care. Think about how perceptions by physicians may have played a role in the findings of a study of cancer patients done by Sandoval, Brown, Sullivan, and Green:

> Among seven common predictors of the overall quality perception across the three models, four should be of particular interest because patients perceived them as relatively problematic aspects of care. These are "was informed about follow-up care after completing treatment," "knew next step in care," "knew who to go to with questions," and "providers were aware of test results." These predictors explained between 25 and 34% of the variance (depending on the model) of the overall perception of quality.[12]

In 2011 the *International Journal of Marketing Studies* published a study exploring the relationship of trust to patient perception of quality care. Not surprisingly, the study found overall that "socio-demographic characteristics were strong predictors of patient satisfaction and patient trust,"[13] generally with those having higher income, education, and other resources reporting higher satisfaction. The study supports the importance of relationships of mutual respect between healthcare provider and client.

EFFICACY

Expanding on Albert Bandura's efficacy research,[14] health efficacy may be defined as the *capacity* to produce a desired or optimal health outcome for an individual, community, or defined population. In this book capacity is defined as a set of nine resources: financial, mental, physical, spiritual, emotional, knowledge of hidden rules, support systems, relationships and role models, and formal register (written, structured, often abstract language).

Efficacy also includes social cohesion, collective knowledge bases and understandings (hidden rules), income inequality, and planning/use of time frames. It is the *capacity* of resources to assist in health. Each of us, at one time or another, has filled a glass of water too full. No matter how much we wanted the glass to hold all of the water, it could not. And that is capacity. In poverty survival tends to be a daily challenge: A number of issues (or crises) occur at once, resources are scarce, and the compounded impact lessens the resources available.

Health Efficacy
Definition: the capacity to produce a desired or optimal health outcome for an individual, community, or defined population

---

Subsets of health efficacy:
- Self-efficacy—resource capacity and belief in one's ability to succeed in specific situations

- Response efficacy—resource capacity and belief that one's action or inaction can create a desired health outcome

- Collective efficacy—shared resources and beliefs that a desired outcome can be achieved by working together
  Types of collective efficacy:
    o Institutional efficacy[15]
    o Neighborhood efficacy
    o Team efficacy

Source: Summary Health Statistics for the U.S. Population: National Health Interview Survey, 2011.

For the purposes of our discussion, we are defining institutional efficacy as the extent to which an institution can marshal resources and inspire the belief in individuals that they can achieve a successful health outcome as a result of their interaction with the institution. Financially strong, sustainable, and even award-winning hospitals or healthcare-provider agencies may not be perceived by some as *able* to help individuals achieve a successful health outcome. They may be proficient in delivering tests, conducting exams, and completing all the necessary paperwork, but none of that guarantees a successful health outcome. Because insurance companies and the third-party payer system typically come between the patient and the "institution," however, there is often an absence of the direct relationships seen between consumers and providers in other service environments.

This way of looking at institutional efficacy can help direct the relationship between the patient and institution ideally to one of mutual trust, respect, and accountability. This definition may better define the relationship between patient and institution for proponents of patient-centered or patient-empowered care.

For optimal health efficacy to exist efficacy would need to be developed. Patient-centered care could evolve, and barriers created by legislation or tradition could be addressed by policy. In the chapters to follow, we introduce how to apply concepts in a different way.

Bandura's look at personal efficacy expectations and outcomes expectations should be further explored to predict and potentially change behaviors specifically as they relate to health and health status. In his analysis "expectations of personal efficacy are based on four major sources of information: *performance accomplishments, vicarious experience, verbal persuasion, and physiological states*" [emphasis added].[16] We include resources as a part of performance accomplishments.

Macro and micro

If those sources of information are transferable to scale, then we can project expectations to the larger institution. Self-efficacy, institutional efficacy, and community efficacy are all interwoven. What happens at the micro level impacts the macro level and vice versa. According to physicist Margaret Wheatley in *Leadership and the New Science,* the "flapping of a butterfly's wings in Japan impacts weather patterns throughout the world."[17] In the health area, along with many others, the discussion centers at the macro level without much discussion at the micro level. Little numbers, however, often become big numbers.

We contend that the four major sources of information cited by Bandura are significantly influenced by economic class. For example, what "performance accomplishments" might someone from each economic class have that would provide coping strategies to face a catastrophic illness? What "vicarious experience" might influence a person from each economic class to select complementary medicine as an adjunct to allopathic care? What type of "verbal persuasion" would be most effective in encouraging patients to be compliant to a particularly challenging healthcare regimen? Identify what words would be used. What might the body language look like? What tone of voice might be used? What are your thoughts about how individuals from certain economic classes or cultures might respond to certain "physiological states"?

Bandura equates the physiological state with the level of emotional arousal. What might we observe in a patient? Resignation? Anger? Is the anger masking fear? How will the integration of those major sources of information predict or change a patient's behavior?

COMMUNICATION

Robert Sapolsky sees communication largely as social coherence.[18] We, however, are going to look at it more specifically in these ways:

- Formal register
- Story structure (the structure of relayed information)
- One-on-one relationships
- Role of non-verbals in a survival environment
- Abstract representational language and constructs
- Impact of time on knowledge bases

All too often the information given by health institutions to individuals in poverty is only partially understood or not understood at all. There is a direct correlation between being poorly educated and poor health.

DISPARITIES IN HEALTH AND HEALTHCARE

A primary purpose of *Bridges to Health and Healthcare* is to offer strategies for addressing the complex issues of disparities in both health and healthcare—and to help build a bridge from those disparities to efficacious health and healthcare.

HEALTH DISPARITIES RESEARCH

It cannot be denied that there are health disparities in the United States. The research focuses in two areas:

1. Health disparities are ***differences among population groups*** (e.g., ethnic, gender, income) in the incidence, prevalence, and outcomes of health conditions, diseases, and related complications of diseases. Groups that experience lower hierarchy in society are at risk of having greater stress. Chronic stressors erode health.

2. Health disparities research also emphasizes how ***living conditions and environments*** influence health outcomes for groups with lower hierarchy:

   - Lower economic status

   - Lower social status associated with racial/ethnic discrimination

   - Individuals employed in stressful working conditions with low hierarchy and decision-making capacity

More specifically:

- How a person develops during the first few years of life (early-childhood development)

- How much education a person obtains

- Being able to get and keep a job

- What kind of work a person does

- Having food or being able to get food (food security)

- Having access to health services and the quality of those services

- Housing status

- How much money a person earns

- Discrimination and social support

- Access to healthcare[19]

Health and Economic Status

Age-Adjusted Percentage Distributions of Respondent-Assessed Health Status, by Selected Characteristics: United States, 2011

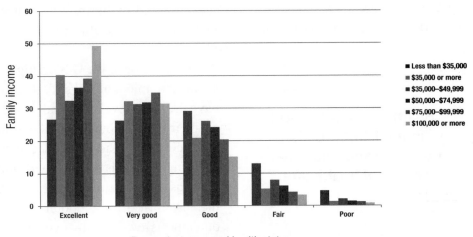

Source: Summary Health Statistics for the U.S. Population:
National Health Interview Survey, 2011.

For a related Health and Economic Status chart, please see Appendix C.

HEALTH*CARE* DISPARITIES RESEARCH

The focus of healthcare disparities is differences among population groups in the availability, accessibility, and quality of healthcare services aimed at prevention, treatment, and management of diseases. These include screening, diagnostic, treatment, management, and rehabilitation services.

Healthcare disparities data consistently show that patients in lower hierarchy groups do not receive the same level of healthcare as individuals with greater hierarchy. This is also the case when the study cohorts included insured patients. The correlation is significant and not entirely due to insurance and access. This research suggests that healthcare disparities are more likely associated with *human interactions* in healthcare settings, rather than insurance or access. ***How the patient is perceived—the perceptual lens of the clinic staff and the healthcare institution—influences the treatment the patient experiences.***

When healthcare professionals are asked if the paradigm or view that their child's schoolteacher has of their child will impact their child's academic performance, most will enthusiastically agree. However, when asked if the health professional's view of the patient or client will impact the health outcomes of the patient, the agreement tends to be less enthusiastic. Healthcare is a science, indeed. But it is also interactive and relational—the *art* of healthcare.

> **Healthcare is a science, indeed. But it is also interactive and relational— the *art* of healthcare.**

People of color in the U.S. in higher socioeconomic circles still do not have the same level of overall health as their white counterparts within that economic class (also see next paragraph). This is documented, and in terms of the entire population, the increased risk of a poorer health outcome is evidenced—even if the person of color is making excellent health choices and following his/her treatment regimen to the letter. Both areas of health disparities research are needed in order to continue the dialogue on both physical environments and social environments, along with the healthcare experience of patients.

African Americans Receive Lower Quality of Care Than Whites

Disparities in healthcare are often ascribed to differences in income and access to insurance. Research has shown these to be important, but they are by no means the only factors. In a 2013 study, the Agency for Healthcare Research and Quality (AHRQ) funded a study in Boston that examined the quality of care provided to hospital patients with congestive heart failure or pneumonia.[20] Quality of care was measured both by physician review and by adherence to standards of care. The AHRQ researchers found no difference in quality of care for patients from poor communities compared with other patients, after adjusting for other factors. They did find, however, that African American patients received a lower quality of care than white patients.

A NOTE ABOUT THE POVERTY RESEARCH CONTINUUM (See Appendix D)

One of the reasons poverty is seldom addressed successfully is because there is little agreement, even in the academic community, about causation. There are four distinct research bases around the causation of socioeconomic class, including poverty, and those research bases have been politicized (see Appendix D).

The research in the Appendix D table needs to be further qualified. Virtually all disciplines move through three stages: classification (naming things), correlation (how things work together), and causation (underlying cause(s). For example, when human beings first noticed the stars, they named them and called it astrology. Then Galileo came along and said the stars move in relationship to each other (correlation), and that became known as astronomy. Then Newton said there is a reason for that: gravity (causation).

The first research base is basically individual choices, the second is community resources (jobs, services) or the lack thereof, the third is exploitation (racism, sexism, predators, etc.), and the fourth is economic and political systems (income inequality, policy, tax structures, etc.).

If you're on the political right, you likely think it's about individual choices and jobs. If you're on the political left, you think it's about exploitation and systems issues. The truth is that poverty is caused by all four factors. Legislative policy often uses only one research base, and then policy tends not to work (again, see Appendix D).

Not only has the lack of agreement of causation been an issue in sociological research on poverty, it is also an issue in healthcare research—lots of agreement around correlation but not much agreement around causation. A significant part of what has been missing from the discussion is what's available through the Bridges approach to class and healthcare.

QUESTIONS FOR REFLECTION

1. How might one's economic class affect access to healthcare?

2. How might healthcare delivery outcomes differ based on the patient's economic class?

3. What resources are not available equally to all economic classes in your community?

4. Do most insured people you know read and understand EOBs (explanation of benefits) from the insurance company? What do most patients understand about costs of services?

5. How do perceptions differ in your community about quality of care at a private clinic with specialized services in an affluent neighborhood versus the public safety-net hospital? What seems to drive those perceptions?

6. Do people from poverty in your community have a voice in decision making when new systems of care are designed for their intended benefit? Does that make sense? Why or why not? If you were designing a healthcare clinic for women, to what extent would you want to hear from women about the design, services, etc.?

7. In this chapter you read, "How the patient is perceived—the perceptual lens of the clinic staff and the healthcare institution—influences the treatment the patient experiences." Have you observed this in your institution? If so, to what degree?

8. Even in a joking manner, has any provider made a judgmental comment about a patient that may have caused you any concern? What did you say or do? Did it make a difference in what kind of care the patient received—or in how timely a fashion the patient was treated?

CHAPTER THREE

EFFICACY: MENTAL MODELS OF ECONOMIC CLASS, RESOURCES, AND HIDDEN RULES

ECONOMIC CLASS ENVIRONMENTS AND THE 'MENTAL MODELS OF ECONOMIC CLASS'

Collective efficacy is defined as a group's shared belief, which emerges from an aggregation of individual group members' perception of the group's capabilities to succeed at a given task.[21] Stated more simply, it's a group's mutual trust and willingness to help each other. Collective efficacy also is a measure of neighborhood social capital and has been associated with positive health outcomes, including lower rates of asthma, assaults, homicide, and premature mortality.

As Emile Durkheim states in the 1893 classic, *The Division of Labour in Society,* the collective conscience is the totality of beliefs and sentiments common to the average members of a society that forms a defined system with a life of its own.[22]

- A specific environment is shared by a large group of people for a significant period of time.

- This shared environment over time pushes individuals within the group toward a collective set of perceptions, perspectives, and priorities. This collective sense of reality defines and sorts what is important from what is less important for the group.

- The collective experience also results in a collective set of understanding considered to be efficient, practicable, and profitable by that population.

Discovering and analyzing Mental Models of Economic Class increase the depth of the dialogue, which becomes more meaningful, much larger, and more comprehensive. The model can be quickly adjusted for accuracy by groups of people, and the entire group will "see" the result and begin to interact with the new information. Using these mental models and looking through a common lens promotes "collective understanding" for individuals, institutions, and communities.

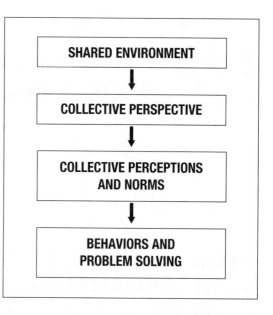

The authors acknowledge that many healthcare professionals are aware of some of the key elements of the economic class experience, but the common lens and the inclusion of people from different backgrounds and experiences in the conversation take understandings to a deeper level.

The Mental Models of Economic Class constitute tools that can help healthcare groups achieve a higher level of effectiveness in the areas of access, availability, cost, and value. Through analysis of these interactions between and among the worlds of economic class, the Mental Models of Economic Class support health teams in identifying points of potential conflict (breaking relationship unintentionally) and develop concrete strategies to avoid economic class collisions that erode (and sometimes shatter) relationships of mutual respect. The models create a quick and effective strategy to start an ongoing conversation that brings something new—and perhaps *someone* new—to the decision-making process in healthcare settings.

The personal lens of societal experience is a flour sifter that filters information and limits perspective. This personal lens is constantly sifting and sorting the important from the less important. Becoming aware of and analyzing our own societal experience helps us to broaden our personal focus and understanding. This is a significant aspect of what *Bridges to Health and Healthcare* brings to the conversation.

Individual personality traits can affect the entire collective environment process and result in outlier behaviors, sometimes called positive deviance. Someone raised in a middle-class environment may have innate qualities, additional protective factors, or some unique quality that may cause him/her to choose differently and live differently from others having a similar experience. The converse is true as well.

Most human beings can identify several groups or environments that have at least slightly different collective efficacy from their own experience. Culture, age, gender, economic class, region, neighborhood, family structure ... All of these contribute to our complex and unique combination of experience. This work simply breaks out the economic class experience from the others so that it can be accurately analyzed, then put back into the mix. Environments do not define us, but they certainly have great potential to influence us.

Individuals in under-resourced environments also can benefit from planning for low-risk behaviors in risky environments. Some individuals in poverty seem almost "superhuman" and can achieve wonderful things despite the fact that the environment of poverty does not provide adequate resources and protective factors. Still, this is not the norm, and to expect individuals in poverty to be "superhuman" is to blame the poor entirely for remaining in poverty.

In this book we are trying to have responsibility for health shared—not only by the person in poverty but also by the healthcare professional, the public health official, the hospital executive—for them to better understand the internally logical rationale and the environmental framework that characterize patients who are survivors of generational poverty. Improving the health outcomes of people in poverty and decreasing health disparities will require more than blaming the individual. It will require implementing policy and system changes that are informed by persons in poverty—and that promote life, prosperity, and healthful behaviors.

THE IMPORTANCE OF RESOURCES

Consider the foundation of resources available in some economic environments, such as the middle class. That foundation includes financial resources that ensure sustainability *and stability* of income, nutrition, leisure, housing, transportation, support systems, program completion in higher education, emotional intelligence, ability to plan, positive support systems and networks, Internet connections, etc. Moreover, many of these skills and aptitudes are inculcated at a very young age.

Most of these resources are eroded by poverty, but the prevailing expectation of the institution and community is that individuals in poverty should achieve the same level of health outcomes and engage in the same positive behaviors as those who have the benefit of such powerful and consistent resources. This perception would be more accurate if decisions and behaviors were solely the result of individual strengths and not influenced by the environment. Bridges is more comprehensive (see the Poverty Research Continuum in Appendix D) and is directed at changing community and institutional environments and the interpersonal relationships that promote health/healthcare disparities. Individuals often need to change, but that isn't the only change that is needed.

Statistics offer some concrete tools to assist in analyzing collective environments of economic class. This analysis of economic class environments is highly abstract and therefore simplified through the use of mental models of economic class. Health teams can use and upgrade the economic class models to fit their own community. These concrete illustrations of environments assist in problem solving and planning at every level, thereby impacting access, availability, cost, quality, efficacy, and communication.

The Mental Models of Economic Class reflect "the way it is now" for individuals within the specified economic class system. The slices of the pie represent behavior and action—and do not judge these or link them to any characteristics. They also reflect how people spend their time to meet the demands of that environment. It is not intended to be representational of internal assets, feelings, personality traits, etc. The mental models simply reflect concrete experience not tied to motivation levels and personal differences. Each mental model, however, shows the driving force needed to survive or thrive within that environment.

MENTAL MODEL FOR POVERTY

Each slice of the "pie" shows how the environment of poverty demands a day-to-day, constant vigilance and the juggling of minimal resources. Agency time reflects the reliance of those in poverty on interaction with social service agencies. It isn't uncommon for a family in poverty to access 20 or more agencies in the period of a year. These include HUD (Housing & Urban Development), workforce development, social services, Head Start, court systems, emergency department, Salvation Army, and so on. Housing is an especially vulnerable resource because the number of affordable housing units trends toward increasingly insufficient affordable units compared with the number of households in

Mental Model for Poverty

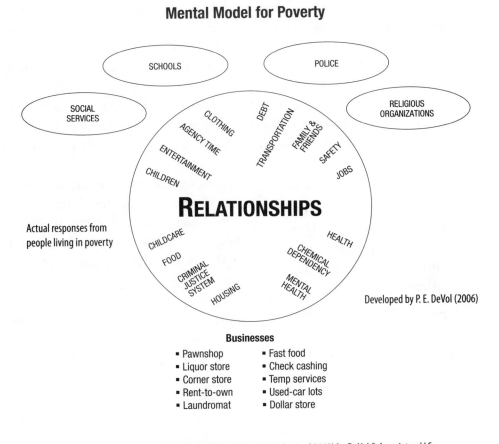

Developed by P. E. DeVol (2006)

Businesses

- Pawnshop
- Liquor store
- Corner store
- Rent-to-own
- Laundromat
- Fast food
- Check cashing
- Temp services
- Used-car lots
- Dollar store

Source: *Getting Ahead in a Just-Gettin'-By World* (P. E. DeVol). © 2006 (revised 2013) by DeVol & Associates, LLC.
Published by aha! Process, Inc. www.ahaprocess.com

need of lower income housing. Education is not represented as a slice of the pie because secondary education program completion (much less postsecondary education) is difficult to access and attain. The four ovals above the pie represent entities that are present in every neighborhood.

It is commonly known that research data define a continuum of experience within poverty. The ability to make the transition out of poverty is relative to the depth and length of poverty for that household or community. U.S. poverty policy since 1998 has largely been designed to get individuals in poverty to work, not to higher education. The popular perception in this country tends to be that people in poverty don't work, but there is a growing percentage of households up to 198% above the federal poverty line (FPL). This group is typically considered "the working poor." Two hundred percent above the FPL is considered a sustainable wage.

The environment of poverty demands quick action, along with creative and adventurous problem solving. How individuals in the environment of poverty solve problems with the tools and resources available to them can be remarkably different from the resources and problem-solving strategies in other class environments. A major paradigm shift for many is to move from "People in poverty are wrong" to "People in poverty are strong."[23] Understanding how problems are solved in poverty is clearly an outcome of developing and analyzing an accurate experience of poverty, as illustrated by the poverty pie chart.

> **A major paradigm shift for many is to move from "People in poverty are wrong" to "People in poverty are strong."**

People in poverty are indeed problem solvers, but the middle-class system seldom celebrates the problem-solving process that poverty itself demands. Consider the experience of resourced individuals, who negotiate the healthcare systems with a tool belt of abstract thinking, higher education, access and knowledge of health websites, personal and professional connections with physicians and other healthcare professionals, formal language skill sets, and other elements apparent in the middle-class pie. This is a rather strong match to the middle-class design of most health-sector services.

Not using the available tools and strategies of the resources of the middle-class environment is generally considered unacceptable. The middle-class resources and skills are usually a good fit with the priorities of the healthcare system.

Most healthcare professionals readily acknowledge that we tend to assume that every patient should be motivated toward healthy behaviors as they relate to quality of life and a healthier future story. The environments of middle class and wealth support the argument for these behavioral changes. What is missing is that poverty does not really offer much experience with quality of life or future story. Poverty offers the focus of survival today—and a future story that is being written as one goes along.

A good starting place is the question: "What are the healthcare-related problems within each economic environment, and what tools are available to solve them?" It is more helpful to look for the strengths and problem-solving capacity of under-resourced patients rather than discuss individual deficits behind closed doors. Better health outcomes help systems avoid the erosion of the financial bottom line because of "frequent flyers" whose lower resources and fixation on the present moment cause unnecessary readmissions and multiple "crises" that often end up in the emergency room.

David Shipler (author of *The Working Poor*) states that it's not so much the "elements of poverty" that define this experience, but the "interlocking nature" of these elements. By this he means that the "vulnerability" of poverty can be exponential, as one resource is dependent on the next.[24] If you lose your car, you may lose your job and your housing in a domino effect. If you become ill and don't have access to a primary care physician, you may continue with increasingly debilitating conditions, such as migraines, toothaches, etc., which affect achievement at school and work. If your partner leaves you, it could quickly snowball into hunger and even homelessness.

This constant vigilance simply to survive has been described as "the tyranny of the moment," Paulo Freire's memorable phrase. When individuals are necessarily focused on survival—and the pressing needs of the day require immediate responses—people find it very difficult to get out of crisis mode long enough to plan for the future. And in poverty, those crises often come in waves.

The reason the word "relationships" is written across the pie is because relationships and the reciprocity of helping one another are critical to surviving poverty or any environment where the other resources have been greatly diminished. A few examples:

- Bartering services (I'll fix your plumbing for some firewood)
- Utilizing a "community car" (someone has one that runs) and throwing in some gas money
- Pooling resources and going to town together for agency time and running errands
- "Doubling up" for a while in someone's house when you have lost your housing (some states count the "doubled up" as homeless)

But there is no guarantee that relationships will be there when you need them.

Mental Model for Middle Class

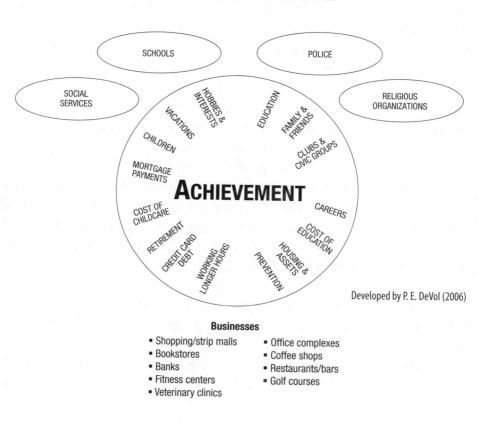

Developed by P. E. DeVol (2006)

Businesses

- Shopping/strip malls
- Bookstores
- Banks
- Fitness centers
- Veterinary clinics

- Office complexes
- Coffee shops
- Restaurants/bars
- Golf courses

Source: *Getting Ahead in a Just-Gettin'-By World* (P. E. DeVol). © 2006 (revised 2013) by DeVol & Associates, LLC.
Published by aha! Process, Inc. www.ahaprocess.com

MENTAL MODEL FOR MIDDLE CLASS

Depicted here is the day-to-day forward movement into future story that is typical of a more resourced life. In these environments, lack of motivation and achievement is not respected. There are usually enough financial assets to afford insurance plans that trump the crises people may experience: house fires, car accidents, death, illness, etc. The emphasis is on the future and outcomes that are linked to increasing stability and sustainability. The future is a daily focus, as is greater freedom of choice that comes with having financial security. Individuals in this environment often work hard and long hours, as do people in poverty. But the "job" in poverty is a "career" in the middle-class environment. A career holds high mobility potential—again with the element of future story embedded. The difference in housing here is that the home is usually a financial asset; future story and increased resources are part and parcel of home and property. The ability to negotiate systems builds professional and social networks through formal-language register that is often used. This insight includes the realization that both public- and private-sector institutions are largely designed from the resourced, middle-class perspective. The system works quite effectively so long as those receiving service also understand and identify with the middle-class experience. But such is often not the case.

MENTAL MODEL FOR WEALTH

This circle illustrates the experience of a select few and typically is drawn from experiences of generational wealth. The experience of recent wealth acquisition (newer money) would fall somewhere between the middle-class and generational-wealth experience, just as the working class (or what remains of that 20th-century American experience) would fall between poverty and middle class. Wealth holds the power and hierarchy missing in the other class environments, as well as reliance on connections. (Relationships help you get by; connections help you get ahead.) The driving force is the maintenance of connections that provide financial and social growth and stability within these circles.

Mental Model for Wealth

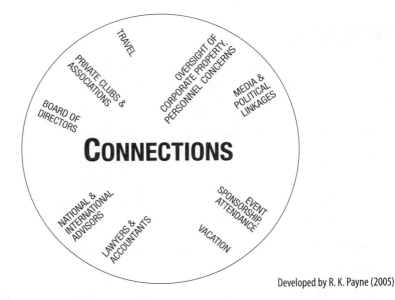

Developed by R. K. Payne (2005)

Source: *A Framework for Understanding Poverty* (R. K. Payne). © 2013 by aha! Process, Inc.
Published by aha! Process, Inc. www.ahaprocess.com

Businesses one sees in wealthy communities include investment firms, private clubs (polo, beach, golf, etc.), exclusive interior-design shops, designer boutiques, high-end antique/consignment stores, artist-owned galleries, spas and salons, 4- and 5-star restaurants, and private schools (preschool through higher education).

It also should be noted that while new and old money often live in the same neighborhoods, they do not think the same way.

HOW YOU SPEND YOUR TIME DETERMINES TO SOME EXTENT YOUR KNOWLEDGE BASE

In looking at these mental models, one can see the difference in the knowledge bases that are acquired simply based on what one spends time doing. Often value is assigned to experience—i.e., one experience is more valuable than another. But the reality is that most experiences can bring strength to an individual to survive a particular environment.

The more generations spent in a given environment, the greater the tendency to use the "rules" that help one survive that environment. Surviving an environment also is dependent upon the resources to which one has access.

NINE RESOURCES

In *A Framework for Understanding Poverty: A Cognitive Approach,* a working definition of poverty is "the extent to which an individual does without resources."[25] The resources are identified as follows:

Financial—Having the money to purchase goods and services.

Emotional—Being able to choose and control emotional responses, particularly to negative situations, without engaging in self-destructive behavior. This is an internal resource and shows itself through stamina, perseverance, and choices.

Mental—Having the mental abilities and acquired skills (reading, writing, computing) to deal with daily life.

Support systems—Having friends, family, and backup resources available to access in times of need. These are external resources.

Physical—Having physical health and mobility.

Spiritual—Believing in divine purpose and guidance.

Relationships and role models—Having frequent access to adult(s) who are appropriate, who are nurturing, and who do not engage in self-destructive behavior.

Knowledge of hidden rules—Knowing the unspoken cues and habits of a group.

Formal register—Knowing the written language of business, work, and institutions.[26]

Financial resources mean you have stable shelter and food. The United Nations defines wealth as having protein in your diet on a daily basis. Food insecurity is reported in 11 million households in the United States. Forty-nine percent of young children in 2011 received WIC (federally funded Women, Infants, and Children nutrition program) food supplements. Hunger impacts thinking and health.

Emotional resources are the ability to not engage in destructive or self-destructive behavior. This is particularly difficult when resources are low because of the nature of survival. If you cannot physically fight or don't have someone to fight for you, survival in a high-poverty neighborhood is very challenging. When you get laid off, do you get drunk? When you're overwhelmed by the social demands of a situation, do you become isolated?

Mental resources mean you can read, write, and compute. If does not mean you have a degree. Do you know if the pharmacist gave you the correct prescription? Can you plan how you will take your medicine? Can you follow the directions on the inhaler? Can you compute the cost of a generic medication over a name brand? Can you buy the correct over-the-counter medicine for a particular ailment? One of us has an educated sister who took Sudafed for plane nausea (oops, wrong thing).

Physical resources mean you can take care of yourself—the daily tasks that determine if you are physically able or handicapped. Can you dress yourself? Feed yourself? Walk? Go to the bathroom by yourself? Get out of bed by yourself? When a person is unable to perform these basic tasks, it then takes someone else to assist him/her. That typically means there is one less wage earner in the household. And the lack of mobility creates additional health issues.

Spiritual resources mean you have a belief in divine assistance and that you have hope and a future story. It doesn't necessarily mean you are religious. There is considerable research about the benefits of prayer in healing and in better health. A future story is critical to staying well. Without a future story, there is little point in changing behavior.

Support systems are the resources that stable households have that under-resourced households find to be very thin. Because monetary value is usually not assigned to this resource, it is often overlooked and ignored. It is a huge issue in health. Do you have transportation to get to the doctor? Do you have healthcare options for your child when he/she is sick? Do you have someone with some knowledge of health whom you can call and get advice? Do you have an older person who mentors you as a parent? Do you have conversations with people who are going through the same kind of thing you are? Do you have someone to whom you can take your child or children for a couple of hours, providing you with a break and a breather?

Relationships and role models are individuals who care about you and vice versa. Ideally, at least a few adults are in the mix. These individuals are nurturing and not damaging to you. Bonding social capital involves people who are like you, while bridging social capital involves people who are different from you.

Hidden rules are the unspoken cues of a group that let you know if you belong or not. At the basis of all emotional wellness is safety and belonging. You always know the rules of the group you were raised in, but you may not know the rules of the group you're moving into. Having knowledge of the hidden rules of at least one other socioeconomic class is an important resource.

> **Clearly, the fewer the resources, the less self-efficacy—and, therefore, the less *capacity* to influence and change your health.**

Formal register is the language used in tests, handbooks, business letters, policy manuals, and medicine. Being proficient with spoken and written English is a key resource. In the healthcare field, specificity of language is absolutely critical.[27]

Clearly, the fewer the resources, the less self-efficacy—and, therefore, the less *capacity* to influence and change your health.

Institutional resources and community resources will be discussed in Chapter 5, which covers institutional and community resources—another aspect of collective efficacy.

HIDDEN RULES

The eighth resource on the preceding list is knowledge of hidden rules. Generally in the United States distinct cueing systems are recognized for racial and ethnic groups, but not particularly for socioeconomic classes.[28] There are many hidden rules—in all three economic classes—to examine.

WHERE AND HOW DO YOU LEARN HIDDEN RULES?

Hidden rules come out of situated-learning environments[29] and are learned by being in those environments; they also are taught. A significant portion of the hidden rules a child learns comes from the parents' or guardians' hidden rules. So if one parent came from poverty and the other from middle class, then the child has the benefit of knowing two sets of rules. Sociologists see this as social learning.[30]

MAKING THE TRANSITION ALONG THE CONTINUUM

When individuals move from poverty to middle class or middle class to wealth, they use part of the rules they grew up with and part of the rules they're moving to. To move from poverty to middle class or middle class to wealth, an individual usually must give up relationships for achievement (at least for a period of time). When one has been in a given group for two generations or more, the rules of that group often are the only rules the person knows.[31]

Hidden rules are important because they impact relationships. One of the key components in making the transition from poverty to middle class or middle class to wealth is developing social bridging capital—in other words, meeting people different from you. When hidden rules are broken, even inadvertently, offense frequently is taken and the relationship doesn't get a chance to develop.[32]

What, then, are the hidden rules? The following chart gives an overview of some of the major hidden rules among the classes of poverty, middle class, and wealth.

HIDDEN RULES AMONG CLASSES

	Poverty	Middle Class	Wealth
POSSESSIONS	People	Things	One-of-a-kind objects, legacies, pedigrees
MONEY	To be used, spent	To be managed	To be conserved, invested
PERSONALITY	Is for entertainment; sense of humor is highly valued	Is for acquisition and stability; achievement is highly valued	Is for connections; financial, political, social connections are highly valued
SOCIAL EMPHASIS	Social inclusion of people he/she likes	Emphasis is on self-governance and self-sufficiency	Emphasis is on social exclusion
FOOD	Key question: Did you have enough? Quantity important	Key question: Did you like it? Quality important	Key question: Was it presented well? Presentation important
CLOTHING	Valued for individual style and expression of personality	Valued for its quality and acceptance into norm of middle class; label important	Valued for its artistic sense and expression; designer important
TIME	Present most important; decisions made for moment based on feelings or survival	Future most important; decisions made against future ramifications	Traditions and history most important; decisions made partially on basis of tradition and decorum
EDUCATION	Valued and revered as abstract but not as reality	Crucial for climbing success ladder and making money	Necessary tradition for making and maintaining connections
DESTINY	Believes in fate; cannot do much to mitigate chance	Believes in choice; can change future with good choices now	*Noblesse oblige*
LANGUAGE	Casual register; language is about survival	Formal register; language is about negotiation	Formal register; language is about networking
FAMILY STRUCTURE	Tends to be matriarchal	Tends to be patriarchal	Depends on who has the money

continued on next page

continued from previous page

	Poverty	Middle Class	Wealth
WORLD VIEW	Sees world in terms of local setting	Sees world in terms of national setting	Sees world in terms of international view
LOVE	Love and acceptance conditional, based on whether individual is liked	Love and acceptance conditional and based largely on achievement	Love and acceptance conditional and related to social standing and connections
DRIVING FORCES	Survival, relationships, entertainment	Work, achievement	Financial, political, social connections
HUMOR	About people and sex	About situations	About social *faux pas*

Source: *A Framework for Understanding Poverty: A Cognitive Approach* by R. K. Payne.

It should be noted that this chart indicates only patterns that may be seen. Many individuals use combinations or parts of the chart. If this chart is used to stereotype individuals or groups—i.e., to assume that everyone in a given group uses these rules—then the chart is misunderstood.

Some explanations and stories may help explain parts of the preceding chart and the following health and healthcare checklists. The bottom line or driving force against which decisions are made is important to note.[33] One of the adult men in an under-resourced neighborhood was very hung over on New Year's Day. He had to go to work the next day. Each year, he got 10 sick days. He said to his wife, "I'm going to call in sick tomorrow." His wife said to him, "No, what if you actually get sick later this year?" And he replied, "What if I die and don't get to use my sick days?!"

The bottom line in generational poverty tends to be entertainment and relationships. In middle class, the criteria against which most decisions are made relate to work and achievement. In wealth, it's the ramifications of the financial, social, and political connections that carry the most weight.

Being able physically to fight or have someone who is willing to fight for you is important to survival in poverty. Yet, in middle class, being able to use words as tools to negotiate conflict is crucial. Many times the fists are used in poverty because the words are neither available nor respected. In poverty there usually isn't the level of education and articulation that one finds in middle class—and especially wealth.

> *"The one deep experience that distinguishes the social rich from the merely rich and those below is their schooling, and with it, all the associations, the sense and sensibility, to which this education routine leads throughout their lives.*
>
> *"As a selection and training place of the upper classes, both old and new, the private school is a unifying influence, a force for the nationalization of the upper classes."*
>
> –C. Wright Mills
> *The Power Elite*[34]

The following checklists—for poverty, middle class, and wealth—illustrate different mindsets and hidden rules about health and healthcare. Again, the following statements illustrate patterns, not blanket statements about any economic class. Maintaining good health requires stable resources and planning.

HEALTH AND HEALTHCARE CHECKLISTS

UNDER-RESOURCED HOUSEHOLDS

Due to the combined driving forces of the moment-driven nature of poverty, strong survival skills, and reliance on relationships, individuals in poverty may utilize and/or identify with the following:

1. At least one person in my household smokes cigarettes.

2. When I am sick, I use the emergency room because I don't have a doctor.

3. Often I don't actually fill my prescriptions because I don't have money for them.

4. If I get sick, it's OK to use the pill I have left over from two years ago.

5. Once in a while I will sell pain prescriptions for money.

6. I know that doctors get a kick-back from the drug companies for the medications they prescribe.

7. My partner/spouse does not like the doctor to see my body.

8. Doctors make fun of you by using words you don't understand, they never listen to you, and usually they get it wrong.

9. If I don't like a doctor, I won't do anything they tell me to do.

10. If I have to see a doctor at night, I usually call an ambulance for transportation.

11. I don't go to a dentist. It's easier to pull my own teeth or have someone pull them.

12. Real men don't talk about being sick or not feeling good.

13. I keep the kids inside the house because it's safer for them there.

14. I don't belong to an athletic club. It costs too much money, and there isn't one in my neighborhood anyway.

15. My children aren't involved in athletics because there's no transportation, uniforms cost money, and sometimes they can play outside at home.

16. I don't eat many vegetables or fruits.

17. When we do go out to eat, we almost always go to fast-food places.

18. I don't have health insurance.

19. I have no idea what I weigh.

20. I don't have my eyes checked often. I just buy "cheaters" at the drugstore.

21. I'm aware that being overweight and even obese is generally OK where I live.

22. I cooperate with healthcare professionals who carefully listen, who don't insist on using big words, and who don't always keep telling me to "Get to the point."

23. I may trust the physician and healthcare providers to hold all of the information, diagnoses, and treatment plans—with minimal questions from me.

STABLE HOUSEHOLDS

Due to the importance of stable life conditions and emphasis on achievement (health success), quality of life, and future story, individuals in middle class may utilize and/or identify with the following:

1. I go to see the doctor on an annual basis for a yearly checkup and blood tests.

2. I belong to an athletic club. I have a membership at a fitness facility (Pilates, yoga, etc.).

3. My children are involved in sports and athletic activities.

4. We have a family physician and health insurance.

5. I fill almost all the prescriptions as recommended by my doctor.

6. If I am sick, before I go see the doctor I often research my symptoms online for information.

7. I use the Internet and recommendations from friends about the best specialists and hospitals to use.

8. I expect my doctor to know who the experts and specialists are in the field, should I need a referral.

9. I have my teeth cleaned twice a year and checked at that time. Any teeth that need additional work are taken care of.

10. I weigh myself at least once a week.

11. I have my eyes checked at least once a year.

12. I often question my doctor about his recommendations and his thinking.

13. When I shop for groceries, I buy fresh fruit, vegetables, and protein for daily consumption.

14. I take vitamins on a daily basis.

15. I check the over-the-counter and prescription medicines for expiration dates and throw out any that I see are past the "use" date.

16. I monitor what my children are eating.

17. When we go out to eat, we will often split a meal and take home what we don't eat at the restaurant.

18. I have health insurance with a high deductible and co-pay—and part of the cost is deducted from my paycheck each pay period.

19. I know my options regarding weight-loss surgery.

20. I know quite a bit about most of the new diet fads.

21. I have tried at least one weight-loss system that has a national spokesperson.

22. I am aware that being obese or even overweight is not generally accepted/respected because obesity does not promote quality of life and future story.

ABUNDANTLY RESOURCED HOUSEHOLDS

Due to the driving forces of connections and the significant power associated with generational wealth, individuals in wealth may utilize and/or identify with the following:

1. I have a "boutique" doctor whom I pay $1500 a year in addition to the visit costs. In return, he/she gives me his/her cell number and takes only 600 patients.

2. I have had Lasik eye surgery and/or cataract surgery and have my eyes checked annually.

3. I have many pairs of glasses and/or contacts in different colors.

4. If I am sick and have to go to the hospital, my doctor meets me there and arranges for immediate care.

5. I have health insurance, dental insurance, long-term healthcare insurance, supplemental insurance, disability insurance, and life insurance.

6. I belong to an athletic club, have a sport or physical activity in which I engage every week, and I have a personal trainer with whom I meet three days a week.

7. I don't eat frozen food. Food is prepared fresh every day.

8. I seldom eat everything on my plate. I don't take food home with me from a restaurant unless I order it to go.

9. I rarely eat fast food. I prefer restaurants where the food is fresh and gourmet.

10. I have my teeth cleaned at least twice a year and have dental implants.

11. I weigh myself nearly every day and have a body mass index in the acceptable range.

12. I don't go to a doctor unless he/she is highly recommended and respected for his/her schooling and expertise.

13. I don't wait in the waiting room for the doctor. He/she sees me promptly at the arranged time.

14. I get extra time with the doctor, should I need it.

15. If I stay at the hospital, I have a private room.

16. I have a personal nutritionist.

17. I know the best spas nationally and internationally to visit when I want to lose weight.

18. I know the best doctors to go to for body sculpting and other cosmetic surgery—and I can easily get an appointment.

19. I am aware that this environment includes social pressure that displays zero tolerance for being even slightly overweight.

The first point about these checklists is that if you fall mostly in the middle class (which is defined as having stable resources), the assumption is that "everyone knows" these things. However, if you didn't know a number of the items for the other classes, the exercise points out how many of the hidden rules are taken for granted by a particular class, which assumes they are a given for everyone.

Accept that decisions will be made against other kinds of thinking than your own.

WHAT CAN HEALTH PROFESSIONALS DO TO ADDRESS THESE MINDSETS AND HIDDEN RULES?

1. First of all, one set of hidden rules is not better than another set. All organisms adapt to their environment. Accept that decisions will be made against other kinds of thinking than your own.

2. Maintaining good health takes times, stability, planning, resources, and knowledge.

3. Institutions—in order to maintain stability—tend to operate according to middle-class norms. So we use an analogy: Basketball and football don't have the same rules. To use football rules in a basketball game is to lose the game. The rules used in poverty at home or in the

neighborhood may be different from the ones used by the hospital or clinic, facility or doctor. Using the institutional rules will help the person from poverty get what he/she needs.

4. Understand that the need for *survival* trumps everything and that survival is a reactive skill—not a planning skill. Following patient-compliance strategies is not the primary focus for adults in generational poverty. Work with the patients to make a plan that will work in their situation. For example, you might consider tying their taking of medicine to a particular TV show they watch each evening.

It might be noted that addressing an issue (such as smoking) so that individuals from poverty can avoid an early death is often not seen as relevant in generational poverty. Death is an unavoidable part of life. Feeling fated is a very common notion. I heard of a teenage male who was criticized for smoking and told he would die young. His reply: "I don't *want* to be an old man. I hope I *am* dead by 50."

What is a motivator for many people in poverty is to do something for the people they love so that those people can stay safe. In other words, appealing to a person to stop smoking so they will be alive to keep their children and loved ones safe has a better chance of success than threats about early death. And, sometimes, asking the patient if there is one thing he/she can change to help keep someone safe is a motivator that results in compliance and cooperation.

QUESTIONS FOR REFLECTION

1. What did I think about when I went through the healthcare checklists? What kinds of emotions or judgments did any of the statements bring up for me?

2. How might having a knowledge of the hidden rules when communicating with a ***provider, family member, caregiver,*** or ***patient/ client*** help improve a treatment plan?

3. If all providers had a better understanding of each patient's resources as presented in this chapter, how might the healthcare delivery outcome be improved? Or not?

CHAPTER FOUR

COMMUNICATION, LANGUAGE, AND COGNITION

LANGUAGE AND COGNITION

One of the biggest barriers to good healthcare for individuals in poverty is the issue of language, the organization of information into stories, and the patterns of discourse. A foundation in Florida that worked with young pregnant teens was faced with a situation in which the teens refused to go to the doctor for prenatal care after the first visit. When asked why they wouldn't go, they said, "The doctor makes fun of us." As it turned out, the young teens didn't understand the words the doctor was using.

To better understand this issue of language, it is helpful to look at the work of Martin Joos (see chart on next page).

REGISTERS OF LANGUAGE

Every language in the world has five registers.[35] These registers are the following:

REGISTER	EXPLANATION
FROZEN	Language that is always the same. For example: medical terminology and procedures.
FORMAL	The standard sentence syntax and word choice of work, school, and the medical community. Has complete sentences and specific word choice—and is usually in writing.
CONSULTATIVE	Formal register when used in conversation. Discourse pattern not quite as direct as formal register.
CASUAL	Language between friends, characterized by a 400- to 800-word vocabulary. Word choice general and not specific. Conversation dependent on non-verbal assists. Sentence syntax often incomplete.
INTIMATE	Language between lovers or twins. Language of sexual harassment.

Source: *The Five Clocks* by M. Joos.

In the medical community, doctors almost always communicate with patients in formal and frozen register, but the majority of patients who come from generational poverty (two or more generations) have difficulty understanding formal and frozen register. They generally speak casual and intimate register. Generational poverty is so isolating that the more generations one is in it, the less access there is to formal register. (The main exception is if the family/individual has a strong religious background. The exposure to written texts of religion provides formal and frozen register.)

Betty Hart and Todd Risley put tape recorders in homes by economic class. They found that a 3-year-old in a professional household has a bigger vocabulary than an adult in a welfare household. In fact, Hart and Risley found that by age 3 children from professional, educated families have heard 32 million more words than children from uneducated families.[36]

Language in Children, Ages 1 to 4, in Stable Households by Economic Group

Number of words exposed to	Economic group	Affirmations (strokes)	Prohibitions (discounts)
13 million words	Welfare	1 for every	2
26 million words	Working class	2 for every	1
45 million words	Professional	6 for every	1

Source: *Meaningful Differences in the Everyday Experience of Young American Children* by B. Hart & T. R. Risley.

The situation in the healthcare setting is further complicated by the fact that most adults from poverty don't have the vocabulary or the knowledge of sentence structure and syntax to use formal register. When conversations in casual register are observed, much of the meaning comes from non-verbal assists, not from word choices. Written communication without the non-verbal assists can be an overwhelming and formidable task, which most individuals from poverty try to avoid. Writing in formal register generally has very little meaning for them.[37]

Medical facilities, as well as the doctors and nurses that staff them, want to ensure that they are free of litigation, so they use precise word choices, and virtually everything—including directions and procedures for the medical care—is in formal register. The problem is that much of it isn't understood by the individuals in generational poverty. Client outcomes, therefore, tend to be dismal, largely because of the lack of understanding.

For example: A patient will say to a nurse or doctor, "I ain't feelin' good" or "That boy is off his feed" or "That medicine ain't workin' no more." When the nurse or doctor asks questions, the amount of specific language or documentation that the healthcare provider wants to hear generally isn't available. Even with questioning, the patient often can't articulate things more clearly. Hence, the nurse or doctor makes inferences about what is wrong. The situation is exacerbated by the increasingly shortened amounts of time that healthcare professionals have with each patient.

Last, but not least, the abstract words are in formal register. Abstract words are the words we use to represent concepts and ideas. When I (Ruby) lived in Haiti, I worked in a "childcare facility," which basically consisted of a table under a couple of trees. We worked with 4-, 5-, and 6-year-olds. A mother came running through the trees with a quart jar of a thick, green slimy substance, grabbed her 4-year-old daughter, and poured it over her head. The little girl was screaming, and there was green stuff in her hair, her ears, and her eyes.

Because French is the formal register of Haiti (the only way to learn it is school, and there is no system of public schooling in Haiti), the mother spoke only Creole, which is the main casual register in Haiti that approximately 95% of the Haitians speak. The missionary who could speak the language talked to the mother who explained that the little girl had awakened that morning with a matted, closed eye. The mother had gone to a native doctor who prescribed the treatment. The missionary explained to me that in the mother's world, the green stuff made a lot more sense than a mysterious or intangible antibiotic because the green substance actually touched her daughter's eye.

And that is the difference between the sensory-based reality and the representational reality. In the sensory reality there must be tangible proof that there is a connection. In the abstract representational reality, the language "represents" the reality. For example, a check is not cash; it represents the cash in the bank account. Another example: The blood-work printout is representative of what is in the body, but it is not the substance in the body.

Much of the language used in the medical field is representational and often isn't understood or used in generational poverty. So when a doctor or nurse describes how to use a particular medicine, he/she will often say, "Follow the directions." Those directions, however, may not be connected with the patient's daily-living issues, so they get ignored.

ABSTRACT REPRESENTATIONAL LANGUAGE

When individuals use formal register to speak and write, they are operating in an abstract representational environment. If a person has mostly casual register, the formal language is not well understood. For example, the doctor may say to a patient that a certain medicine needs to be ingested with food and that blood pressure will be elevated if the directions aren't followed. To the doctor, the language is very clear. But the patient who has only casual register may have no idea what *ingested* and *elevated* mean—even if he/she was born in the United States. To make the conversation clear, the patient in some instances needs to receive information on a page with two columns—one with the words and one with a drawing. The drawing will translate at a practical level, and the words will help the patient understand the doctor or the nurse.

STORY STRUCTURE

Complicating the situation with language is the manner in which information is given. In formal register, story structure usually has a beginning, a middle, and an end—and the story revolves around plot. So during a story, listeners will ask, "And what happened next?" The story is organized around cause and effect.

Formal-Register Story Structure

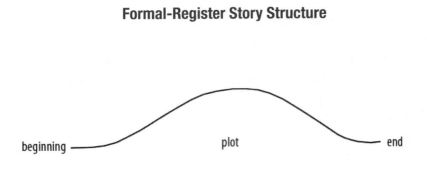

But in an oral tradition, typically in casual register, the story starts somewhere close to the end and is episodic and random in structure (it is how many of us gossip). The story revolves around characterization. So during a story, listeners will say, "He did that? She said what?" The story is organized around emotional significance. It is seldom chronological.

Casual-Register Story Structure

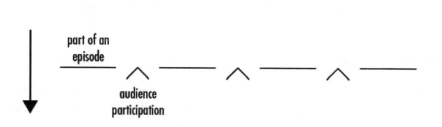

What happens in the medical profession is that the healthcare provider expects the patient to provide a formal-register story structure so the professional can determine cause and effect. Individuals in generational poverty, however, usually provide the story in casual-register story structure—telling the parts that have the most emotional significance to them and in episodic, random order. This kind of storytelling takes much longer to get to the "basics" of the issue. But many healthcare professionals don't have that kind of time, so they interrupt the patient and make a guess as to what the health issues are. These interruptions and the accompanying non-verbal messages can start to erode the patient's trust in and connection with the caregiver.

Furthermore, these stories are almost always participatory, with multiple tellers. The broken horizontal line in the preceding drawing represents the episode, and the carats represent the interjected comments from the audience.

EXAMPLE: A man in his 20s comes into the emergency room with a broken leg.

> ***Healthcare provider:*** *How did this happen?*

> ***Patient:*** *You know Carl's been workin' on that car of his forever, and he had it up on cinder blocks. A skunk got under the car and had babies there. Well, the dogs didn't like it one bit. They was goin' crazy, so I got out my gun to get that skunk.*

Patient's relative: I told Carl he shouldn't put the car there. That raccoon has been hanging around those houses. You know, that one where they left and trashed the place before they moved out. Well, that raccoon took up livin' there, and it was one "busy" raccoon. Had babies more than once. And then a skunk decided to live there too and came across the lot to have babies under the car.

Healthcare provider: So how did your leg get hurt?

Patient: I'm trying to tell you.

Patient's relative: You gotta know that Johnny ain't the most coordinated person alive. I told him he shouldn't be handling that gun while he's under the car.

Healthcare provider: Did the car fall on your leg?

Patient: Well, I crawled on a nail first and got it in my arm. And then my cousin Ronnie came over.

Healthcare provider: Was the nail rusty?

Patient: How the hell would I know? If I saw that nail, I wouldn't have crawled on it. I didn't know Carl had boards on those cinder blocks. And Ronnie's as big as a horse, and he eats like one too. So when I crawled on that nail, I took a painkiller that Ronnie gave me.

Healthcare provider: How long ago did you take the painkiller, and what was it?

Patient: Something Ronnie had. I don't know what it was, but it worked pretty quick. Then I got dizzy and lost my balance. About that time the skunk did his number on Ronnie. And that made Ronnie mad, and Ronnie mad ain't a pretty picture.

Patient's relative: Yeah, one time Ronnie got mad, and he picked up a cinder block and threw it 20 feet into the window of the neighbor's house. That neighbor didn't bother him no more.

At this point, the healthcare professional gives up trying to find out what happened and assumes that somehow, in some way, the car fell on the patient's leg.

This would be the same story in formal register.

> *There was a car in the neighborhood on cinder blocks, and a skunk got under the car. The dogs were trying to get to the skunk. Johnny brought out a gun to shoot the skunk and crawled onto a nail, injuring his arm. Johnny's friend, Ronnie, gave him a painkiller, which made him dizzy, and he fell down next to the car. Then the skunk sprayed Ronnie, which made Ronnie mad. Ronnie then picked up one end of the car so the dogs could go after the skunk, but in trying to watch the dogs he dropped the car. The car didn't fall back onto the cinder blocks but rather it fell on Johnny's leg and broke it.*

In reading this story, many individuals have commented that the formal story structure had information that the casual story structure did not and vice versa. That is correct. The emphasis of each is different. The formal story structure emphasizes plot and cause/effect. The casual structure emphasizes characterization and emotional significance. It is also much more entertaining! Often "asides" about the person or situation—totally unrelated to the story—are inserted for their entertainment value.

HOW CAN HEALTHCARE PROFESSIONALS ADDRESS THIS?

It isn't uncommon to see discharge instructions strewn all over the pavement and lawn outside the hospital emergency room or clinic entrance. People in generational poverty are used to receiving "meaningless" stacks of paper in a variety of institutional and agency settings.

It isn't uncommon to see discharge instructions strewn all over the pavement and lawn outside the hospital emergency room or clinic entrance.

Creating a mental model of the disease

The purpose of the two mental models that follow is to prepare patients to take charge of their disease management from the moment they leave the facility.

The following sequence is important. The first mental model of the patient's condition is to be used by the patient to teach family members about the disease/condition and the importance of proper disease management. The second mental model helps patients anticipate the problems they will face when they are "under their own care" and have solutions and supports in hand, ready to be used.

In this method the models are created by both patient and caregiver, working shoulder to shoulder. When the models are done well, the patient will not discard the paperwork but will likely ask for a copy to take home. The caregiver can give the original to the patient, make a copy for the facility's records, and assure the patient that the caregivers are part of his/her support team.

- Is the disease progressive, chronic, and/or fatal?
- What are the stages and symptoms of the disease?
- What are the signs of relapse?
- What are the typical time frames?
- How can all this be represented in a mental model?

In the ensuing example of congestive heart failure, the patient has marked her experience on a time line. The precipitating event was at age 63, but information from the past shows weakening heart strength. The disease management practices of salt/sodium, weight, and medication will stabilize the condition. If the disease isn't managed well, the patient can expect to have trouble breathing, feel weak and tired, and will no doubt be coming back soon to the hospital.

All of these things should be drawn by the patient as she talks through her understanding of her disease. As she talks through this with the caregiver she is "teaching back" to the professional. When she goes home she will be "teaching forward" to her friends and family.

Some patients may indicate which events they want to experience in the next 15–30 years: the birth of grandchildren, annual family reunions, etc. The connection between relationship and future story may be the primary motivation for individuals who identify with "relationships" far more than "achievement."

The goal here is for the patient, not the professional, to be making the argument for his/her own care and management.

Features of the disease (common considerations) that will help develop a mental model include:

Mental Model for Progression of Congestive Heart Failure

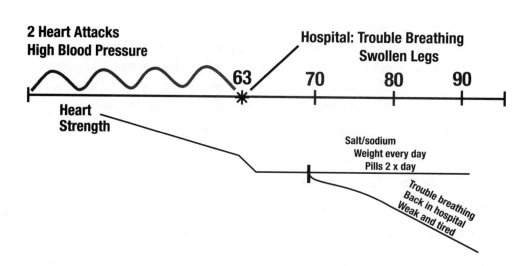

Developed by S. D. Garee & P. E. DeVol (2012)

Creating a mental model for disease management

The next mental model prepares patients to think through what needs to be done in several areas of their life to take care of themselves adequately. Remember that people living in unstable environments like poverty often will have a hard time with the destabilizing effects of stressful, low-paying jobs; transportation problems; childcare; crowded housing; poor sidewalks and few parks; lack of street lighting; access to good food; low social coherence; etc.

In the following model (on page 70):

1. The age line establishes a future orientation.

2. The three sections for past, present, and future create space for mental models in each.

3. The three sections below the horizontal line are for notes, reminders, to-do lists, etc.

4. The Stability Scale (see Appendix F) appears at lower left in the chart in order to name the problem of stability if it comes up. The less stable the situation, the harder it is to manage the disease.

5. The mental model of a support team is to be developed after making the mental model of the future.

Steps for developing the mental model of the future:

1. Explain that you will be working on a plan that patients can use from the moment they leave—something they can show to family members, along with the mental model of the disease.

2. Mark your age the on the line.

3. Work on the "present" by talking about what patients can expect to encounter when they leave your care:

   - Who will pick you up?
   - Who is living with you?
   - What do they know about your disease?
   - How do you think they will they react to the plans you make?
   - Will it be difficult for them to support you? Why or why not?
   - How will you pay for and get the prescriptions you need?
   - What about meals, mobility, etc.?
   - Who will be your biggest supporter or supporters?
   - Who probably will not help much?

   Have the patient represent each person on the page with circles/initials or symbols; offer encouragement to place the people close to or far away, according to his/her feelings. Have the patient make notes in the space on the next page.

4. Work on the "past" if necessary.

   - What were things like earlier?
   - Was it better or worse at some points?
   - How have things changed for the people you mentioned?
   - What was the stability factor like then?

   Have the patient make notes in the space on the next page.

5. Work on the "future."

   - How do you need the future to look in order to be successful in the long term?

- What do you need from yourself and others (including family and healthcare providers)?

- Cover necessary medications, access to those medications, exercise, diet, work, transportation, childcare, aged care, others living in the house, pets, etc.

Have the patient draw in the characters and discuss the realities. Again, make notes below.

6. Develop the "support team" mental model by creating a set of circles with the patient in the center and adding supportive people and organizations around the patient. These are only those people who will support them the most. Those individuals would need to know about this plan. Again, the patient uses the mental model to "teach forward."

7. Make copies of the mental models for your records, saying you will be checking back on this with the patient (only if this is true, of course).

Mental Model for Disease Management

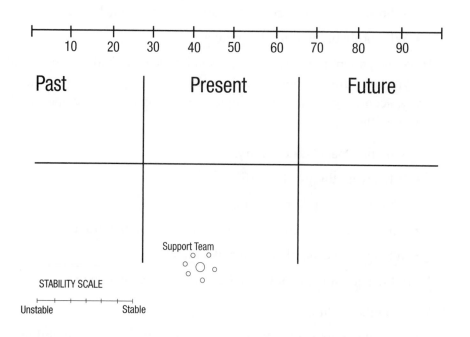

Developed by S. D. Garee & P. E. DeVol (2012)

QUESTIONS FOR REFLECTION

1. What would be at least three different ways of using mental models to help educate a patient, client, or family member?

2. How is the institution for which you work (or go to for care) meeting the national standards for culturally and linguistically appropriate services (CLAS)?

3. How might the material in this chapter help institutions meet those standards?

For website information on CLAS, see Bibliography entries National CLAS standards and Notices (same keywords as in Endnotes).[38]

PART II: COURAGEOUSLY CROSSING THE BRIDGE

CHAPTER FIVE

INSTITUTIONAL AND COMMUNITY RESOURCES— COLLECTIVE-EFFICACY EXAMPLES AND APPLICATIONS

Individual, institutional, and community intersections have great synergistic potential, but when we add policy to the mix, great ideas and noble intentions can be quickly and significantly eroded in the process.

INDIVIDUAL, INSTITUTIONAL, AND COMMUNITY RESOURCES

Individual	Relationships	Physical	Financial	Mental
Institution	Staff/people	Facilities	Financial	Information and data
Community	Inter-relationships of social, service, government, business organizations	Physical infrastructure	Financial capital	Technology, innovation, capital, education resources

Resources are the foundation for all the research bases. These resources take on a multiplier effect when institutional and community resources are added.

INSTITUTIONAL RESOURCES QUIZ

Please identify which of the following statements are true for your institution.

1. The staff is poorly trained and has frequent turnover.
2. There are long waits for the patient to be seen.
3. The staff is stressed, overworked, and generally indifferent to patients.
4. Cost cutting appears to be the primary goal of management.
5. Many services are outsourced.
6. The staff is current with research and is knowledgeable.
7. Many staff person are new to the profession.
8. The technology is out-of-date and functions poorly.
9. A living wage is not given to the hourly staff; many staff are part-time.
10. Employee benefits are given only to salaried workers.
11. All appointments are scheduled; if a person is late, he/she is not seen.
12. Front-line staff persons are included in the decision-making process.
13. The buildings are clean, the restrooms are very well-kept, and hand sanitation is readily available.

Emotional/spiritual	Knowledge of hidden rules/language	Social support	Motivation/integrity/trust
Culture/future story	Institutional hidden rules	Human, financial, and environmental support systems	Credibility/reputation
Inclusion and civility for all; future story	Cultural, historical, geographical patterns of interaction	Community infrastructure	Quality of life, commitment to well-being of all

14. The staff is polite to patients and readily answers questions.

15. The staff is respectful to patients who are older.

16. Patient advocates are provided for each patient.

17. Training is provided in cultural and economic diversity (racial/ethnic, economic class, gender, age) and is evidenced in patient treatment.

18. Explanations are given for each treatment, medication, and surgery.

19. Waiting-room amenities are provided without cost.

20. A chaplain is available for your faith.

21. Staff is trained in grieving and issues of hospice and dying.

22. Staff is trained to deal with unruly patients and visitors.

23. The institution provides security that is discreet, yet effective, and does not impede access to staff.

24. Staff openly discusses patient issues with non-family members.

25. After a patient rings a bell for service, it can take up to an hour to get help.

26. The dignity of the patient and his/her caregivers are the driving forces of the institution.

27. The institution has a positive presence in the community.

28. The institution has an endowment that also sponsors charity fundraising events for the institution.

29. Policy design and procedure are keys to the institution's success.

30. The institution is known for attracting excellent clinical staff and other professionals.

31. The institution is affiliated with a research institution and may have a clinical education and training component.

32. The institution has payment options for all economic levels—for example, sliding-scale fees, scholarships, etc.

33. Staff is adequate (not understaffed) and usually functions well as a team.

34. Records are haphazard and not easily obtained.

35. Controlled substances are carefully monitored and accounted for.

36. Although HIPAA (Health Insurance Portability and Accountability Act) laws are "followed," much patient information is obtained in cubicles where others can easily hear.

37. Dispensing of medicine is controlled and tracked.

38. The institution has a streamlined method of communicating patient information to the patient's primary healthcare provider.

39. On weekends, the quality of staff is significantly less capable and services (e.g., labs, imaging) are significantly reduced.

40. The emergency room is chaotic, poorly organized, unclean, and often rude.

41. The staff "parties" in the hospital and is poorly supervised.

42. The institution has a responsive customer complaint department.

43. The institution's polices are not enforced on a day-to-day basis.

44. The institution's website is well-developed and responsive to patients' needs and questions.

45. The institution accepts Medicaid and Medicare, as well as individuals with insurance.

46. It is frequently not possible to get a live person on the phone in less than 10 minutes.

The preceding questions give a perspective on the resources of an institution. These are coupled with the resources of a community (following quiz).

COMMUNITY RESOURCES QUIZ

Please identify which of these resources are available in your community.

1. Our community has a 20- to 25-year plan for community development.

2. Public transportation is available in all parts of the city/county/ community.

3. Our community has a sufficient number of doctors and medical institutions for our population.

4. Bike and running paths, parks, soccer fields, playgrounds, etc., are available throughout the community.

5. Wellness facilities (gyms, tennis courts, exercise facilities, golf courses, pools) are easily accessible.

6. Our convenience stores have synthetic nicotine available in candy for under-age individuals.

7. Police protection is not readily available in high-poverty areas of our community.

8. Our domestic-violence, homicide, and suicide numbers are higher than other communities.

9. Our community has facilities and organizations that serve individuals with addictions and mental illness.

10. Our community has facilities and services for the disabled, the handicapped, and the aged.

11. Our community has a community endowment; multiple, active service organizations; and an effective chamber of commerce.

12. The schools in our community have a better-than-average graduation rate (in terms of the national average), generally high achievement, and an excellent reputation.

13. Our community has a newspaper, TV coverage, and Internet access for under-resourced individuals, all of which provide useful information about good health.

14. Our community has a homeless population that heavily utilizes the library.

15. The roads and infrastructure of our community are well-maintained.

16. Crime is low in our community.

17. Affordable housing is available in our community.

18. Living-wage jobs are available to most residents of our community.

19. An individual in our community can get "medical help" 24 hours a day without accessing the emergency room.

20. Ambulances are frequently used just for transportation in our community rather than for emergencies.

21. Dental services are mostly unavailable—even to those with Medicaid—because of dentist availability and/or transportation.

22. Many individuals from poverty in our community buy most of their groceries at convenience stores.

23. The rates of obesity and diabetes in our community are higher than the national average.

24. Medical facilities have individuals who can translate for our immigrant population.

25. Our community has a readily available list of organizations and agencies that can be accessed for assistance or explanation.

All of the preceding institutional and community resources are linked to one or more of the six healthcare research bases: access, availability, cost, quality, efficacy, communication.

COLLECTIVE EFFICACY

Together, the resources and areas of research lead to collective efficacy. In other words, is the *capacity* available to make the changes necessary to better health and healthcare—at all three levels: institutional, individual, and community? And then, does policy support those changes?

> *"The stronger the perceived efficacy, the more likely are people to persist in their efforts until they succeed."*
>
> –Albert Bandura

According to Bandura, "The capacity to represent future consequences in thought provides one cognitively based source of motivation. Through cognitive representation of future outcomes individuals can generate current motivators of behavior."[39]

Further, Bandura found in his studies that strength of efficacy predicts behavior change: "The stronger the perceived efficacy, the more likely are people to persist in their efforts until they succeed."[40]

In exploring health efficacy, the social ecological approach (SEA) provides a complementary conceptual framework to the work of *Bridges to Health and Healthcare.*

Social Ecological Approach

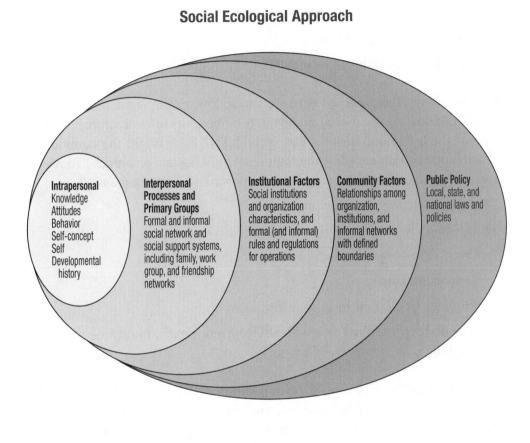

Intrapersonal
Knowledge
Attitudes
Behavior
Self-concept
Self
Developmental
history

Interpersonal Processes and Primary Groups
Formal and informal social network and social support systems, including family, work group, and friendship networks

Institutional Factors
Social institutions and organization characteristics, and formal (and informal) rules and regulations for operations

Community Factors
Relationships among organization, institutions, and informal networks with defined boundaries

Public Policy
Local, state, and national laws and policies

Source: "The Social Ecology of Health Promotion Interventions," *Health Education Quarterly,* K. R. McLeroy, A. Steckler, & D. Bibeau (Eds.).

In building bridges to health, we believe that elements of community infrastructure listed below influence relationships between *individuals* and *institutions,* and, when considered appropriately, can improve the probability of achieving health efficacy at the community level:

- Community assets
- Housing
- Education systems
- Road infrastructure
- Civic engagement

- Childcare
- Employment
- Environment
- Economics
- Social/cultural determinants
- Neighborhood isolation or inclusion

When reviewing the observed behaviors to follow, examine them through the lens of these questions: To what extent might community infrastructure influence some of the behaviors attributed to individuals? How might the community infrastructure be influenced by the individual thinking and resources? To which economic class are the following behaviors ascribed most frequently?

- Arrives late for appointments
- Is a no-show
- Overuses emergency rooms instead of clinics
- Is noncompliant
- Provides incomplete or false information
- Substitutes prescribed care with advice from friends, family members, neighbors, co-workers, or Internet

To explore opportunities to strengthen institutional efficacy and create implementation strategies for a healthier community, we could explore the following by asking such questions as: To what extent might community infrastructure influence some of the behaviors attributed to institutions/agencies? How might these be experienced or addressed by members of each economic class?

- Hours of operation
- Complicated forms
- Redundant questions/processes
- Perceived rudeness or apathy of staff
- Treatment/outcome disparities
- Fragmentation of care
- Delays with few updates or explanations
- Excessive time in waiting room
- Bills difficult to understand

EXAMPLES OF WHEN COLLECTIVE EFFICACY DOES AND DOES NOT HAPPEN

In the following examples, you can see the effects at the intersection of individual, institutional, and community resources—and then the concomitant complications from policy.

EXAMPLE: MARK KRAMER AND ATUL GAWANDE CONNECT THE PIECES

A clear representation of connecting the pieces of institutional efficacy with community efficacy to create health efficacy can be found in a conversation between Mark Kramer and Atul Gawande.[41]

(Mark Kramer is co-founder and managing director of FSG and is a consultant, speaker, and frequent contributor to *Harvard Business Review* and other publications; Atul Gawande has written extensively on medicine and public health and is a highly respected surgeon, journalist, and expert on safety and efficiency in surgery.)

Mark: *It seems like no individual doctor, hospital, or insurer can bring about these kinds of changes. Instead, a neutral party, like a foundation, has to bring all the parties together to solve the problem collectively. In fact, there are often perverse payment incentives that discourage improvements in care because the savings to one party come at the expense of another.*

Atul: *Right. Take a topic like asthma in the inner city, a very big problem affecting children. Children's Hospital here in Boston recognized the problem and decided to start a project focusing on the kids with the most severe asthma attacks, who came to the emergency room or were admitted to the hospital.*

They said, first of all, let's identify what great care looks like for those kids. And essentially they came up with a checklist: a half-dozen things that can make a big difference, ranging from home visits to make sure there was no mold and mite infestation in the house to making sure a nurse checked in and the family had actually filled their prescriptions for inhalers and knew how to use them. They even bought families vacuum cleaners, because they found a quarter of families in the inner-city areas did not have them. After one year, the number of asthma admissions to the hospital emergency room dropped 80 percent. It was a stunning success. But guess what the number one source of revenue for Children's Hospital of Boston is? Asthma admissions. That's how the hospital makes its dollars. And if a place has to choose between doing the right thing and going bankrupt, that's not much of a choice at all.

So even though Children's Hospital found a solution, they couldn't implement it without changing the reimbursement system. They went to their major insurers—Medicaid and Blue Cross—and said, Here's what great care looks like. We've proved it, and it can save you a lot of money, because the extra cost of these services is a lot less than the cost of hospital admissions. But we need to renegotiate our contract so that we're paid for providing great care, even though these kids aren't being admitted to the hospital.

And they worked out a deal. Neither the insurer nor the hospital could have solved the problem alone. But, working together, they recognized a problem, they found a solution, and then they addressed it. This is what a great coalition can do at the community level in a way that you'll never invent in Washington.

Mark: *So you are saying that the hospital can't do it on its own, the community can't do it on its own, and the insurer can't do it on its own. It can only happen through collaboration.*

Atul: *That's right, and even though Children's Hospital renegotiated for themselves, that doesn't mean that asthma care for kids who go to other hospitals in the community is going to change, let alone kids in other communities across the country. Here's a solution that could save significant dollars for the health care system and save kids' lives, but it's not going to happen unless we focus on the larger picture. That takes collaboration, and the problem is that those kinds of collaborations almost never happen. It takes a community leader to bring the medical, business, and government communities together to find solutions and figure out how to fund them.* "[42]

In this conversation, Kramer was offering an opportunity for philanthropists and other donors to help effect change. Any neutral party, taking a community leadership role, could convene various groups. Each health system knows what drives its highest expenditures. Anyone who has studied healthcare economics knows the relationships of trends in practice patterns to changes in payment/reimbursement policies. Health efficacy can be achieved only by "focus on the bigger picture."

EXAMPLE: FASHION AND DIET INDUSTRY

Let's explore a socially oriented initiative. In *Self-Efficacy: The Exercise of Control,* Bandura discusses the fashion and diet industry:

> Part of the effort to ameliorate the epidemic problem of dieting and eating disorders should be directed at raising collective efficacy to alter sociocultural values and standards of physical attractiveness that breed health problems and self-devaluation. The socially oriented approach targets the unhealthy sociocultural values as the problem needing change. The media must be sensitized to the fact that the svelte models of beauty they propagate create severe pressures on young women to try to conform to this ideal of femininity. The pressure of social forces on the marketplace may also help to exert a corrective influence on the fashion industry, which parades spindly models as the cultural ideal.
>
> The fashion industry may well be forced to alter its standard of beauty by changing demographics in which the median age of the population with expendable income is rising and women are pursuing careers in which knowledge, intelligence, maturity, and wisdom are the valued attributes. These social changes are not lost on advertisers. In the world of fashion modeling, vacuous pubescent anorexic models are being replaced with middle-age models portraying images of mature women closer to reality. Yet the multibillion dollar diet industry has a vested interest in preserving thinness as a cultural ideal for women. These marketing forces, allied with media purveyance of svelte images and remedies, are in all likelihood important contributors to the recent advent of bulimia as well as its perpetuation.[43]

Although unlikely partners, the media, diet industry, and fashion industry could—were there the will and the ability to incentivize heath efficacy—help create a different result from what we have today. Actually stepping forth in that direction, the Council of Fashion Designers of America (CFDA) created a health initiative in January 2007 "to address what has become a global fashion issue: the overwhelming concern about whether some models are unhealthily thin, and whether or not to impose restrictions in such cases."[44]

Continues the CFDA: "Working in partnership with the fashion industry, medical experts, nutritionists, and fitness trainers, the CFDA formed a committee to propose a series of positive steps designed to promote wellness and a healthier working environment."[45] Their recommendations include requiring models with eating disorders to get professional help and developing workshops for the industry about eating disorders.

The outcomes for this effort are not yet available. The experience, however, has provided opportunities for evaluating how strategies have been implemented by disparate partners.

EXAMPLE: ELLIS MEDICINE

Using the Bridges key concepts/constructs at Ellis Medicine in Schenectady, NY, allowed every department—and every level within those departments—to look through a different lens at the work they do every day.

The first step in the Ellis process was to develop an accurate Mental Model of Poverty for Schenectady. For public health workers and healthcare providers alike, there is a movement toward understanding a clearer vision of the needs of the under-resourced patient population.

Bridges provided Ellis with a more focused and intentional strategy, with concrete models, tools, and nomenclature that enabled groups of professionals within the system to focus services through the lens of economic class (environment, availability of resources, and healthcare options for patients).

Clearly, being underinsured and under-resourced differs from the experience of patients within a stable environment, which includes much greater availability of resources and healthcare options.

Ellis revised its current outcome-tracking tool to identify, measure, and explore avenues to address barriers to care experienced by individuals and families in poverty. The goal was to surround patients in poverty with a system that listened and responded to patient needs across the board in a comprehensive manner.

As part of this focus, the Ellis team relied on the Bridges Mental Models of Economic Class, which were particularly helpful in determining the concrete experience of individuals in poverty in the community. Team members compared and contrasted the environments of economic class and the resources available in the economic experiences, including insurance, and also the driving forces of those environments.

Ellis Medicine identified that it needed to add and incorporate multiple lenses that included the changing needs of patient populations at risk of health/ healthcare disparities. Ellis came to a consensus on a new Theory of Change, namely: "Identifying the changing needs of our patient population and looking at ways to address those needs and/or modify our service delivery."

Ellis chose to utilize systemwide redesign. The primary strategy was to develop new perspectives and procedures so that patients in poverty would be "heard" by their caregivers, just as patients who are better off engage in positive relational experiences with clinical caregivers, insurance enrollment staff, and so on. In the two years following the introduction of the Bridges Out of Poverty constructs at Ellis Medicine, here are the results:

- There has been a reduction in the use of the emergency department (ED) for primary care, and the unnecessary hospital readmissions that will not be reimbursed as the Affordable Care Act (ACA) is rolled out.

- Kellie Valenti, vice president of Strategic Planning and Program Development, saw this clearly and presented the "business case" for using the Bridges lens, tracking how the model would impact the ED and unreimbursed readmissions, as well as other measures that Ellis' system is tracking.

- Under the leadership of Valenti, the Ellis ED has developed a model with multiple lenses that incorporates Bridges understandings of the hidden rules of poverty, the tightrope walk of resources available to those in poverty, and other Bridges concepts/constructs.

Ellis Medicine works hard at bringing everyone to the table—and using the talents and experiences of individuals from all economic classes. Danielle is a graduate of the City Mission Getting Ahead class and of the Schenectady City Mission program. (Getting Ahead grew out of the Bridges effort.) When Danielle presents to the ED staff, she tells from her perspective what it's like for a single parent in poverty to access the Ellis emergency department with her kids. She also shares her family's challenges in the journey to access and attain a sustainable life, health, and wellness.

As a team, Danielle and the Ellis health navigators share updated information on community resources and provide the ED staff with quick, effective ways of identifying the patient's missing resources. The patient is then given a follow-up appointment—within hours or days—with a primary physician at the Ellis Medical Home. Transportation and other resources are put in place. The ED and other departments have adopted the Bridges concepts to (1) personalize information, (2) use mental models and diagrams, (3) amend written and verbal communication to more casual registers, and (4) seek first to listen and understand. All this results in bringing standard patient/staff interactions to a more effective and informed level.

Shifting ED patients to the primary care at the Family Health Center has resulted in fewer ED visits for primary care in the two years Bridges has been put into practice.

Building trust begins with every staff member on Monday morning and continues as a long-term strategy. Two illustrations:

- Every patient who leaves the Ellis ED has an appointment with a primary care physician in the near future.

- When the appointment is made with the patient, staff will intentionally bring a personal and casual flavor to the interaction, for example: "Oh, I love that doctor—I think you'll like her too. How's everything else going? I'm a social worker. So transportation to the Family Health Center is tough? Well, we have about five options here for transportation."

The focus of the organization is to not degrade or denigrate decisions made by patients, even if the decisions don't always make sense in terms of middle-class health outcomes and "the system." But what is encouraged—and what all Ellis workers hold themselves and one another accountable for—is the idea of mutual learning.

Furthermore, at Ellis patients in poverty are informing the staff about the best approaches to reach individuals in marginalized groups—what really works and what could be improved.

Relationships with the community organizations have increased, and the "silos" that are typically present in communities are replaced with respect and mutual growth. Ellis does not impede the funding and expertise of community agencies that are trying to meet certain outcomes to maintain and increase funding.

At Ellis there is the scope of influence that each agency brings to bear; every organization is the expert in its sector. For example:

- The Schenectady Community Action Program (SCAP) is located onsite at the Ellis Health Center campus, providing patients with access to services related to basic needs such as housing, clothing and food; SCAP also assists with accessing governmental benefits, such as SNAP (food stamps) and heating assistance.

- Ellis provides cab vouchers to the Department of Social Services for patients in need.

- Schenectady City Mission also will provide shelter almost immediately and temporarily if at all possible.

- Ellis Medicine can't bend the Section 8 wait list for affordable housing, but it can assist with a diagnosis; sometimes if a patient has been identified as having a disability, he/she will be moved up the list.

Finally, everything is designed from the perspective of relationships and the continuing growth of individuals in the system to build trust and respect in diverse economic class interactions. The relationships between staff and under-resourced patients have become a priority at all levels. Ellis Medicine has embedded aha! Process's Bridges to Health as part of the organizational ecosystem of the institution. The relationships of mutual growth and mutual respect with almost 40 community partners involved in wrap-around services have been designed from a perspective of mutual learning, growth and sustainability for individuals, for the institutions and their community.

> **The relationships between staff and under-resourced patients have become a priority at all levels.**

Four Ellis Medicine results following the introduction of Bridges constructs:

- Ellis improved standing in the Robert Wood Johnson Foundation ranking of healthiest counties in New York for three consecutive years.

- The percentage of uninsured patients treated at the Ellis Family Health Center Emergency Department declined from 20% to 18% as the hospital enrolled more patients in Medicaid.

- The patient volume at Ellis primary care clinics increased 25% over two years as more patients visited the clinics rather than the emergency department.

- More than 340 people without primary care physicians established care at the Ellis Family Health Center.

EXAMPLE: MOBILE MAMMOGRAPHY VANS

Many of us are familiar with the era when several hospitals invested in mobile mammography vans to go into housing developments. They rolled forward—providing access, availability, quality, and cost-effectiveness using nurse practitioners. Most did not have the positive results initially hoped for. Why? Because the goal was a priority for the hospital and providers, not necessarily for the intended beneficiaries.

On one occasion, the Assisi Foundation of Memphis, Inc. was approached to fund a clinic in a housing development for a local hospital located close by. Although the intent had merit, the original plan did not include any input from the residents of the housing development. The foundation suggested the hospital consider hiring a cultural anthropologist to survey the residents about the idea as part of a broader interview. The hospital agreed, funding for the survey was approved, and Ciaramitaro & Associates began interviewing the residents.

The residents had much to say. They were more concerned about personal safety, the immediate environment's influence on their children, personal finances, employment opportunities, and family matters than whether or not they could have an onsite clinic. During the survey process, some even accompanied a group to Chicago to look at Bethel New Life to see how that housing development had changed. For one of the participants, it was her first trip by plane.

The hospital didn't have Darling and Randel's checklist (see their eight points later in this chapter), but what it implemented (after the interviews and assets assessment were completed) certainly addressed most of the elements on the checklist. Among the results cited in the 1998 American Hospital Association NOVA Award to St. Joseph Hospital for its work,

> the housing complex became a safer place to live, after faulty smoke detectors were replaced and a police substation opened—by one measure, crime actually dropped an astonishing 77 percent. A 24-hour nurse triage service was begun, and funds were found to launch an asthma education center. Job training programs were

created, among them "Families First," credited with finding work at St. Joseph for several Lauderdale Court residents.[46]

These activities were accomplished with less expense than renovating space and staffing a clinic, with the added benefit of creating multiple positive community relationships that otherwise would not have been made. The hospital has since been sold, and the expansion of St. Jude Children's Research Hospital stands where the hospital and its school of nursing once served the community. Fortunately, the lessons of the collective efficacy experience among St. Joseph Hospital, Lauderdale Courts, and other community partners still remains. To build healthcare efficacy, an additive model of exploring individual, institutional, and community resources is essential.

INSTITUTIONS AND COMMUNITIES

Collective experience within the diverse environment has been the focus of health research for decades. Some environments are devoid of the numerous protective factors that offset many of the stressors of life. Different environments lead to different perceptions; different perceptions lead to different perspectives; and different perspectives lead to different choices, behaviors, and problem solving.

The marginalization of some groups results in populations that have limited perceived power/locus of control in navigating the dominant society. The perception of those subgroupings is fundamentally accurate. There is a large body of evidence that supports the influence of collective experience (environment) on individual behaviors and health outcomes within groups or populations.

FIVE PROCESSES OF EFFICACY

Using social cognitive theory, the individual acquires knowledge as his/her environment converges with personal attributes and experiences. With the acquisition of that knowledge, each of the resources listed contributes to building self-efficacy. How does it work? Bandura identifies five processes

> by which efficacy beliefs generalize across domains of functioning. The assessment implications of a process-oriented approach can be illustrated with achievement of generality in self-efficacy through use of serviceable self-regulatory skills. This contributor

to personal efficacy would be assessed by multifactor scales of perceived self-regulatory efficacy to plan and structure activities; to enlist needed resources; to regulate one's motivation through proximal challenges and self-incentives; and to manage the emotionally and cognitively disruptive effects of obstacles, setbacks and stressors. Empirical evidence that efficacy beliefs vary across activity domains should temper the pursuit of a psychological Grail of generality, however.[47]

INSTITUTIONAL EFFICACY

Much of the focus in healthcare is around institutions. Understanding institutional behavior can often be challenging, particularly when attempting to differentiate the media marketing message from the actions taken by the individuals at the institution and analyzing the multiple factors influencing decision making. Mathematica Policy Research published a white paper in October 2012 that helps define institutional behavior seen in the current environment.

> Organizations that employ physicians can manipulate the work environment in other ways that reward certain clinical decisions; these tactics include allocating (or withdrawing) talented support staff and making it easy or difficult to order tests or consultations. Other mechanisms to influence desired point-of-care decisions include procedures for recruiting and/or retaining affiliated physicians, allocating professional amenities (access to state-of-the-art medical technology, opportunities for travel and advancement), and the specialty focus and practice style of the physicians chosen for leadership positions in the organization.

> Large provider organizations will not necessarily be more committed to evidence-based decision making than will solo practices. Even among academic medical centers, which are committed to both research and the application of science to medical care, clinical practices can deviate substantially from current available evidence (Ayanian & Weissman, 2002). Policymakers should therefore assume that large provider organizations, like any other large enterprise, will respond to the incentives presented to them and act to influence their employees' decisions at the point of care according to their own interests.[48]

INSTITUTIONAL EFFICACY AND FINANCIAL INCENTIVES

Bandura's paper also describes how current financial incentives in the fee-for-service system lead to both the overuse and underuse of services at the point of care by physicians and other clinicians. Further, it explores how prominent payment reform options may reward more evidence-based clinical decisions.[49]

The conceptual model developed by Rich et al. depicts the organizational influences on point-of-care decisions.[50]

Organizational Influences on Point-of-Care Decisions

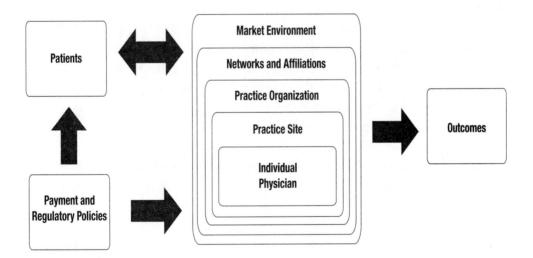

Source: "Paying Wisely: Reforming Incentives to Promote Evidence-Based Decisions at the Point of Care" by E. C. Rich, T. Lake, & C. S. Valenzano for Mathematica Policy Research for Center on Health Care Effectiveness.

The chart above identifies multiple areas that impact collective efficacy. Health reform by whatever name—Affordable Care Act, fee-for-service incentives, changes in reimbursable services, etc.—is challenged by each of these interactions.

Institutional efficacy is an essential element in building health efficacy. Typically "institution" is seen as "organization." Dr. Leah Curtin, executive editor of *American Nurse Today,* describes organizations this way: "Organizations are surprisingly complex structures that function as living, nonlinear, dynamic systems. They illustrate quantum principles that don't lend themselves to observable phenomena."[51]

INSTITUTIONAL RESOURCES REQUIRED FOR EFFICACY AND QUALITY

To build institutional efficacy, organizations as they existed traditionally (or what they may evolve to be) are inevitably perceived by individuals and communities in certain ways—for better or for worse. The following points are offered as complementary and desirable institutional attributes.

Staff/people: Employees of the institution are mission-oriented. They are highly skilled, knowledgeable, open, respectful, courteous, and compassionate. Each staff person graciously responds to the equivalent in his/her setting of one of the most common questions asked at Disney World: "What time is the 3 o'clock parade?" Each employee understands his/her value to the mission.

Facility: The facility is well-designed, safe, and well-maintained. Signage is clear, and it's easy to find specific offices or places within the facility.

Financial: The organization has sufficient operating and reserve funds.

Information and data: Technology is current or even cutting-edge. Evidence-based research is used. Practice to produce evidence is encouraged, with appropriate management of risk.

Culture: This is an ethical, learning organization with transformative leadership. Continuous quality improvement is a way of life. The organization empowers and supports individual efficacy.

Environment: The space is clean and inviting. The use of light, color, and spaces is harmonious. People experience the environment as peaceful and nurturing.

Community relations: The organization seeks opportunities to collaborate with and support identified community needs. The organization makes decisions.

Credibility/reputation: The organization is a trusted partner.

INSTITUTIONAL CREDIBILITY AND REPUTATION

Because relationships of mutual respect and trust are so important in the work of Bridges Out of Poverty at the individual level, the concept of trust at the institutional level merits further explanation. Rowe and Calnan explore the changing dynamics of the trust relationship in healthcare. Tracing the trust relationship historically between patient and provider, they outline shifts that include both interpersonal and institutional trust.

> *The shift towards more informed patients willing to participate in decision-making we would argue has produced greater inter-dependence between patient and clinician. This has not removed the need for trust in clinical encounters, rather trust is now more conditional and negotiated and depends on the communication, provision of information, and the use of "evidence" to support decisions. This is particularly important in the management of many chronic diseases such as diabetes where success depends at least as much on changes that the patient can make, requiring a partnership between patient and health care practitioner.*

> *The realization of such new forms of trust of course requires greater communicative competence on the part of clinicians. The ways in which clinicians interact with service users have to change, providing information and supporting their participation in decision-making requires greater communication skills and may result in longer or more consultations. It also depends on patients' willingness and ability to adopt a more "active" stance, and whether they have access to the resources (finance, time, and energy) to do this. Just as interpersonal trust is more conditional so is institutional trust. Rather than assuming that high standards of care will be provided, the public increasingly requires information that this is the case.*

In countries like the UK where public trust in the health system is believed to be in decline the political response has been to seek to use performance management as a mechanism for rebuilding public trust. Rather than relying on traditional processes of professional self-regulation to ensure high standards of competence and conduct, governments are increasingly turning to external agencies to regulate, monitor, and publicly report on the quality of care. The use of health technology assessment agencies in standard settings to encourage the provision of care that is clinically and cost effective, and of external regulators such as the Healthcare Commission in the UK to assess quality of services, act to provide visible reassurance that services are being monitored and that standards of care can be relied upon.

The public reporting of an organization's results (in terms of meeting targets such as waiting times, patient satisfaction, and clinical outcomes) also in theory enables patients to make an informed choice about where to seek treatment. Such public disclosure of performance is designed to rebuild public confidence in health care organizations but ironically this very mechanism further undermines trust. Clinicians distrust managers' efforts to meet centrally determined targets, fearing that it will reduce their autonomy and ability to [prioritize] treatment according to patient need. Patients are [skeptical] about the reality of performance figures in light of evidence of managers' "gaming" the system to meet targets.

Indeed, we would argue that low levels of trust are implicit in performance management approaches to governance with their increased monitoring and surveillance of professional behavior inevitably causing a decline in trust within organizations and between health services.[52]

COMMUNITY RESOURCES FOR COMMUNITY EFFICACY

In *Leadership for Healthy Communities: Characteristics of Healthy Communities,* David L. Darling and Gayla Randel list the following:

Human resources: This refers to the individuals who make up the community and their learned skills that create the ability to lead teams of people, manage systems and produce goods and services. The sum of these skills among all residents as well as in-commuters equals the human capital available to tackle community issues.

Physical infrastructure: These are the public and private investments that are permanently affixed to the land in the community such as water, sewer and phone systems, homes and office buildings. Monetary resources can flow from one account to another.

Financial capital: They finance community, economic, and business development projects. Financial capital for business use can be classified as seed, venture or expansion capital.

Technology innovation capital: This is devoted to supporting the creation of new technologies and the transfer and commercialization of new innovations that are created from it. These new technologies can be applicable to both the private and public arena.

Capacity to change: This is defined as the financial, human and other types of resources devoted to planning and implementing community and economic development efforts. New organizations can be invented or adapted to support people, firms and agencies involved in the process. An example is a community foundation.

Business environment: This is the general support or lack of support given to local firms by local government, labor markets, foundations and others who impact the environment. Examples like building codes and zoning ordinances can positively and negatively affect the local business environment by encouraging or discouraging expansion or relocation.

Natural and environmental resources: The purity or lack of purity of water, air, soil and other dimensions of the environment are examples of environmental resources. Forests, coal and fisheries are examples of natural resources.

Quality of life: This inclusive concept is the set of recreational, cultural and amenity factors people can enjoy locally.[53]

To identify the degree to which the characteristics identified by Darling and Randel translate as community resources, the Community Assessment tool developed by DeVol & Associates, LLC in *Getting Ahead in a Just-Gettin'-By World*[54] also can be used to create a mental model and a basis for examining the case studies (see Chapters 1 and 7) found in this book.

INTERSECTION OF INDIVIDUAL, INSTITUTIONAL, AND COMMUNITY EFFICACY

Prior to work in recent years, most health-related literature looked at issues from the perspective of either individual behaviors or structural characteristics. Stephens, Markus, and Fryberg suggested a new model:

> The sociocultural self-model begins to bridge this individuals structure divide by focusing on how individuals and structures mutually influence each other and by recognizing that they are best analyzed together. Beyond the principle of mutual constitution, the sociocultural self-model takes into account how people's previous life experiences shape their understandings of who they are and who they envision themselves to be in the future. Further, it delineates how these particular understandings guide how people make sense of their worlds and how they interpret and respond to a given situation.
>
> Taking these insights into account means that behavioral change cannot occur in a vacuum or with a "one-size-fits-all" approach. Effectively encouraging individuals to complete homework or to eat vegetables requires also considering whether these behaviors are relevant or meaningful to the socioculturally shaped selves that are relevant in the situation. If the desired behavior (e.g., completing homework) is not viewed as self-relevant or as part of one's self, then this model provides a blueprint for considering what changes are necessary for the desired behavior to become self-relevant for the person in that situation.
>
> By providing these insights to supplement the traditional individual and structural models, the sociocultural self-model allows for a more complete understanding of the types of behaviors (e.g., unhealthy diet, academic disengagement) that play a role in generating inequality and, in turn, provides the tools to develop effective and self-sustaining interventions.[55]

Further, the Institute for Healthcare Improvement's Triple Aim (not to be confused with the Bridges triple *lens*!) initiative is a framework that encourages the development of new designs of healthcare delivery "to simultaneously pursue three dimensions:

- Improving the patient experience of care (including quality and satisfaction)

- Improving the health of populations

- Reducing the per capita cost of healthcare"[56]

For more information about Triple Aim, please visit *http://www.ihi.org/Engage/Initiatives/TripleAim/Pages/default.aspx.*

This book, *Bridges to Health and Healthcare,* proposes that the intersection of individual, institutional, and community efficacy has the potential to drive policy-level change to effect "triple lens," enterprise-level change.

WHAT CAN AN INSTITUTION AND A COMMUNITY DO TO CREATE COLLECTIVE EFFICACY?

EXERCISE: INAPPROPRIATE EMERGENCY ROOM USE

As an exercise, think about one of the common banes of hospitals—inappropriate emergency room (ER) use. Typically the complaints are about those who are uninsured or underinsured, using the ER like a clinic. Recent studies, such as the one by Sommers, Boukus, and Carrier, however, have found that this may largely be a myth.[57]

Then there are the "frequent flyers," those patients known to make multiple visits for non-urgent visits. Some will acknowledge why many people, often the "working poor," use the ER during evenings and weekends. Whatever the facts, exploring the reasons for inappropriate use, applying the resources graph, and using DeVol's Community Assessment tool may be additional means of helping to build the collective efficacy necessary for sustainable solutions. For each proposed strategy, what might be done to create financial incentives for the institution, build self-efficacy, modify institutional "behaviors," and create the collective efficacy for long-term solutions? What changes must be made?

For example: What would it take to provide case management for frequent fly-ers? Healthcare administrators know how to staff a hospital 24 hours a day, and clinical administrators are proficient in creating effective staffing strategies. Have we ever wondered …

- Why couldn't we triage patients and send individuals appropriately to a "clinic" within the hospital (staffed during evening hours and weekends) and others as appropriate to the emergency room?

- What could be done to adequately staff "health department clinics" for extended hours and, at the same time, make them environments where people feel they can achieve a successful health outcome without extensive waiting periods?

- Why can't health department clinics be open during evening hours and on weekends?

- What are the differences in cost to provide "primary care" in the emergency room versus providing primary care in a clinic or primary care setting?

- Why not do the analysis of both direct costs and opportunity costs?

- How would community behaviors need to change?

- What infrastructure—like public transportation, geographic locations, etc.—must change?

- What policies would need to change?

- How might changing behaviors that add unnecessary and extraordinary costs to the system become "self-relevant" to the individuals taking those actions?

Obviously the "fit" may not always be as clear as we might like. The main result of this process could be that our thinking will be challenged enough to stimulate more creative and effective solutions. There are plenty of examples, of course, of failed programs that healthcare providers designed, which may have sounded logical and reasonable at first blush.

One of the key principles of the Bridges model is the importance of having under-resourced people "at the table" when plans are being made and policies are being established. Most healthcare providers have heard about this concept, but we often feel too pressed for time, we forget, or we think "we know best." For more information on ways to bring individuals in poverty "to the table," please visit *www.ahaprocess.com/gettingaheadnetwork.*

QUESTIONS FOR REFLECTION

1. Based on the quizzes in this chapter, which resources do you seem to lack in your institution? In your community?

2. What policy changes are needed to support the capacity necessary to improve health and healthcare delivery outcomes in your institution? In your community?

3. As you reflected on the questions posed throughout this chapter, which ones seem to be easier to address within your sphere of influence? For the more challenging, to which individuals, groups, or institutions might you be able to reach out to in order to effect change at any level (institution, community, or policy)?

4. Were you able to think of any budget-neutral strategies for change that might work in your institution? Community? If so, what strategies?

5. After reading the various examples about efficacy in this chapter, what came to mind about potentially applying the constructs to your setting?

6. Which organizational influences seem to have greater weight regarding point-of-care decisions in your institution? How do you think that affects outcomes?

CHAPTER SIX

BUILDING RELATIONSHIPS: SOCIAL COHERENCE, SOCIAL COHESION, AND SOCIAL CAPITAL

"No problem can be solved from the same consciousness that created it. We have to think with a new mind."

–Albert Einstein

Population health research links lower social hierarchy and position—low levels of power within work, institutional, and/or community settings—and health disparities.[58] Embedded within the social determinants of health is the concept of power and perceived locus of control. The research is clear that personal power and "voice" are linked with more positive health outcomes. Lower power/hierarchy—where decisions are made for an individual within a work-related or community system—is associated with the stress that impacts health, a factor in health and healthcare disparities.

At the individual level, the argument is strong for educating people to enhance their emotional skills, language skills, and other internal assets to assist in their ability to navigate systems. There is no argument with the personal power that comes with building this individual capacity. Yet if the re-

> **Social coherence can best be described as social resonance between a system and the populations the system engages.**

search on social determinants of health is accurate, it then becomes necessary for the system and environment to also change—i.e., for institutions, communities, and policymakers to genuinely include the voice of the under-resourced in decision making in every possible way in order to move toward health and healthcare equity.

The research of best-selling author and Stanford professor of neurobiology, Robert Sapolsky, illustrates that social coherence is critical to building relationships at every point of contact within the health system. Social coherence can best be described as social resonance between a system and the populations the system engages.[59]

Sapolsky concludes that social coherence is a primary contributing factor to persistent health disparities once access and availability have been established. If a subgrouping of the population does not identify with the dominant culture— and, for our purposes, the dominant culture is the middle class, which we define as "stable resources"—power and hierarchy are thrown way out of balance.[60] Sapolsky's social coherence theory is central to the Bridges lens.

Health messages, like those of other sectors, tend to be based on "stable resources" perspectives and resources. It is logical that the stable-resourced environments perceive the messages as meaningful. What happens when another critical mass of patients or clients does not identify with the resources, values, assumptions, and collective experience of stability? We can use the Bridges lens to view the potential clashes that rise out of this social dissonance.

POTENTIAL SOCIAL DISSONANCE BETWEEN/AMONG ECONOMIC CLASSES WITH REGARD TO HEALTH AND HEALTHCARE	
Collective efficacy generated by **poverty** (under-resourced) environments and systems	Collective efficacy generated by **middle-class** (resourced) environments and systems
"Do you see me? Do you see us?"	"We're good? Great. Let's get down to business."
The Continuum of Instability: Poverty is on a continuum in terms of co-morbidity. Correlative data link the long term, and extreme poverty increases co-morbidity of multiple risk factors.	**The Continuum of Stability:** At minimum, most resources are intact or above average; insurance provides a safety net.

continued on next page

continued from previous page

POTENTIAL SOCIAL DISSONANCE BETWEEN/AMONG ECONOMIC CLASSES WITH REGARD TO HEALTH AND HEALTHCARE	
Driving forces—relationships and entertainment: Both will get us through this thing.	**Driving forces—achievement and outcome:** Goals for both patients and systems are merged in developing access, availability, cost, and value.
Time is on a general continuum: The insight of David Shipler: It's not so much the elements of poverty, but their interlocking nature.[61] Lower resources in multiple areas leads to vulnerability. There is often a real current crisis (housing, food, job, car, etc.), and two more in the wings. Who can mitigate this? "We'll get there when we can." General preference for open scheduling.	**Time is absolute and structured; being on time and using time efficiently are related to cost and respect:** Scheduled appointments rather than open scheduling. "No, thank you. I don't want to come during open scheduling. Would you give me an appointment time, please? Good, that would be wonderful. I would like to minimize the wait time."
Diminishing resources to survive: Long-term, lower-resourced poverty does not usually offer the tools and resources needed to navigate the achievement-centered, outcome-based (access, availability, cost, value) design of most health institutions and other systems.	**Stable resources to thrive:** The resourced environment emphasizes the value of long-term stability. The messages tend to promote a positive future story. For systems, the pitfall is assuming all patients have the minimum level of middle-class resource kit available to complete treatment plans.
Caregiving in the "tyranny of the moment": Planning for the future, caring for the sick family member with one hand while juggling and stretching insufficient resources with the other. If a loved one is at high risk of infection, pets, children, household environments, etc., must be controlled. The under-resourced caregiver must juggle and stretch resources that are already insufficient.	**Caregiving in long-term resourced stability:** It is never easy, but the resourced caregiver is more likely to have strong financial and social resources to manage care of a loved one and other day-to-day concerns. Keeping environments safe when a loved one is ill is time-consuming but doable with higher resource levels. Housing, food, and transportation are not constantly sabotaging forward progress.
Focus on relationships: The focusing on relationships when other resources are minimized is a strategy used to problem-solve in many different areas of life.	**Self-sufficiency:** When a problem arises, the resourced caregiver/patient will have language and other resources to navigate the system. This may include persistence, questioning professionals, and working with the patient advocate with calmness and confidence.

continued on next page

continued from previous page

POTENTIAL SOCIAL DISSONANCE BETWEEN/AMONG ECONOMIC CLASSES WITH REGARD TO HEALTH AND HEALTHCARE	
Language and communication: Approaches formal situations with concrete informality, including language, circular story structures, participatory communication ("You know that I'm listening to you if I keep adding my comments as you speak"). Typically feels comfortable with at least 10 minutes of informal time before getting down to business.	**Language and communication:** No more than two minutes of casual socialization are typically tolerated before getting down to business. Communication is expected to be succinct and sequential. Frustration is experienced when patients don't "get to the point."
Navigation: Tries to relate personally if the system personnel are liked. This is the best strategy to getting what you need. Offers to share lunch with the clinical staff, tells funny stories or jokes, quick-witted, shares very personal information so staff will feel bad and help more. May get angry and want to argue when loved one is not being properly cared for.	**Navigation:** The middle-class environment promotes and undergirds every possible resource and skill to navigate any given system. This is illustrated by how Elizabeth negotiated with Francis' caregivers (see Chapter 1).
Focus on concrete, tough, basic survival: Survival undergirds everything. Present are survivor's pride and respect of individual strengths and persistence.	**Focus on systemic survival:** Recognizes need for patient-driven care, but abandons these because of systemic demands. Respects collective-impact community planning and strategies but is driven by cost constraints. Planning and future projections, goals and objectives provide collective structures for future orientation of the system. Has achiever's pride in finding a better outcome or future story.

Source: T. Dreussi-Smith.

According to Sapolsky, health systems must be highly motivated and intentional about building social coherence in order to build relationships.[62] By default, institutions in all sectors are set up for fail/fail. Under-resourced patients and clients may have different perceptions of medical messages, treatment plans, preventive medicine, and behavioral health messages; these may not be seen as meaningful. When this occurs, institutional outcomes suffer, and reimbursements are withheld.

SOCIAL COHERENCE

Sapolsky says all this collective environmental dissonance is a clanging cymbal. He calls it "noise."[63] Noise is the *Blah blah blah, yada yada yada, wah wah wah* we all hear when we sense that the person or institution has no clue about our experience, our situation, our priorities. It is a description of how dominant culture messages sound to those who don't identify with that experience.

Sapolsky also focuses on relationships and information flow—but actually, this is an issue of hierarchy and "voice." He draws an indelible connection between "voice," locus of control, information flow, and social capital/relationship to health and healthcare disparities.[64] The Bridges lens informs health systems how to work toward better social cohesion between stable and unstable resource systems. It is the fundamental Bridges belief that individuals in poverty are problem solvers who need to be "live and in person" at the decision-making table in order for social cohesion to be truly achieved. The core of relationships is shared voice and mutual respect.

Interaction

Give examples of middle-class health "change messages" that can be perceived as "noise" to those who may not identify with the dominant economic class or culture.

Developed by T. Dreussi-Smith (2011)

What does social coherence look like?

The basic strategies offered by Sapolsky to improve social coherence[65] intersect the Bridges work strategies designed to build relationships of mutual respect. The Bridges lens has provided traction for medical systems as they become more intentional about building social cohesion. The strategies include:

1. Decrease "noise" and retool health messages to be more meaningful to individuals who are under-resourced or whose resources are unstable.

2. Embed relationships of mutual respect where information flows both ways.

3. Establish "voice" or elevate perception of hierarchy; include at the decision-making table individuals from poverty and other groups at risk of health disparities.

4. Design effective tools layered in every department and formally engage community partners to quickly address missing resources. If patients/clients feel respected, it is more likely that health messages will at least be considered as something important, because someone with whom you have established trust is presenting this information.

5. Use a brief assessment to quickly determine if the patient has the necessary resources to follow the treatment plan, preventive medicine regimen, etc. Even if a relationship is present between the institutional staff and the patient, missing resources will likely result in fail/fail.

EXAMPLE—URBAN PREGNANCY PREVENTION

An example of "noisy" messages would be at an urban high school where a prevention educator was presenting a module on pregnancy prevention. The high school had a very low graduation rate.

The educator, newly trained in Bridges Out of Poverty, was using a strategy called "If you choose, you may have chosen." This strategy focuses on choices, potential consequences, and future story without a lot of "noise." The educator said to her group, "Consider this: If you choose to get pregnant, you may also have chosen not to go to college." The educator was drawing some skeptical looks, and someone laughed out loud. "Miss," the amused young woman said, "you are nice, yeah, but are you stupid? Who sittin' here is gonna graduate and go to college? Are we Harvard material?" Lots of laughter.

The problem was not the tool. The problem was the middle-class achievement-based outcome that was expected to motivate young people who had little to no access to that experience. The educator shifted quickly and said "OK. You fill in the blank. If I choose to get pregnant, I have chosen _____ … what?"

Everyone was looking around, and finally a hand shot up. "I'll tell you how it is. If I choose to get pregnant, I got four children under the age of 5." The educator said, "I'm confused. You have no children." The young woman said, "My mother and me are stayin' with her sister and her cousin. And between all of them there are three little kids, and who has to be their babysitter? I can figure this out: If I have my own baby, I just got one more reason to never get outta there and have a good time."

How can you build relationships if there is little basis of understanding your own societal experience—and how undeniably achievement-driven are most of the messages and procedures in every sector? Are we missing the mark with the populations most at risk of poor health? You don't have to assume anything about anyone, stereotype anyone, and definitely never judge anyone. The tendency to assign negative characteristics to behaviors and assign "lack of motivation" to populations at risk of health disparities is not a strategy.

The bottom line on building relationships is to seek to understand someone's experience and perspective, to give him/her the platform on which to build trust, and to make the argument for his/her own change. Bridges strategies seek to engage the group, client, or patient in problem solving rather than make that person's argument for change *for* them.

> **Bridges strategies seek to engage the group, client, or patient in problem solving rather than make that person's argument for change *for* them.**

SOCIAL COHERENCE AND RELATIONSHIPS OF MUTUAL RESPECT

Nancy Garth, BSN, RN, CLNC, FCNs, and Dr. Linda Alexander, EdD, are sisters employed by the University of Kentucky. Both are strong Bridges to Health advocates and have reframed how they approach their work based on the Bridges constructs.

Garth is a health education coordinator at the University of Kentucky Polk Dalton Clinic & Family Care Center and has worked extensively in clinical environments that primarily engage patients in poverty. Dr. Alexander is an associate professor in the Department of Health Behavior.

When describing social coherence and the need to establish relationships of mutual respect, the two tell of a number of cases where medical teams assumed incorrectly that resources were present, and health outcomes consequently were compromised.

EXAMPLE—A REMOTE APPALACHIAN AREA

In one example in a remote part of Appalachia, a mother brought in a 3-year-old with a severe ear infection. The physician explained that the infection was serious and noted the need to see the boy again in three days. The physician wrote the prescription for the mother and explained how to administer it. At the pharmacy, the pharmacist made sure the mother understood that the medication wouldn't work if the child drank grapefruit juice.

She arrived home to find that her teenage daughter had gone grocery shopping and used all the money they had until Friday. Grapefruit juice had been on sale for 75% off. They were practically giving it away! The well pump was broken; there was no running water. They had milk, but if she gave the boy milk there would be no milk for everyone's cereal. Milk is food, and at times cereal was all they had to eat for days. The mother didn't want to waste the medicine, so she didn't give it to the boy.

When she brought the boy for his follow-up, the physician was alarmed that the infection was much worse. After hearing this story, the physician and clinic staff brainstormed strategies to ensure that this wouldn't happen again. They linked the family to a local resource to immediately assist the family.

The point of the example is that most institutions, in health and in other sectors, will struggle if they default to the following assumptions:

1. Patients are motivated by the messages of stable, resourced environments.

2. Patients have the resources to complete the treatment plan.

3. Patients often tell providers that there are missing resources that will hamper treatment success. Typically, many under-resourced individuals won't say anything about the lack of resources.

The focus on achievement/outcomes is twofold: improve health/wellness and conserve costs so the institution is sustainable. If health practice is designed from the perspective that resources are stable and predictable, the focus on relationships—which may be the top priority for under-resourced patients—is going to have a deleterious impact on the institution's sustainability.

How patients perceive the healthcare system and how those in the system perceive the under-resourced could provide some ways to address healthcare disparities. A pediatrician who has been using the Bridges framework and concepts for many years noticed that under-resourced parents of neonatal intensive care unit (NICU) babies tend to be less likely to give up and stop all treatments, even though quality of life for the infant is gone.

The emphasis for any group whose collective efficacy is based on relationships and survival is more likely to focus on the relationship, not on the health condition or quality of life. Those in the stable financial environment of the middle class and wealth are more likely to have experienced a higher quality of life and are in terrible emotional pain about the outcome, yet may have a more abstract and broader understanding that the health conditions are truly critical and are having a devastating effect on this little individual.

At a forum in a Midwestern hospital about such issues, a healthcare provider mentioned her frustration that those in poverty would want to continue the treatment and procedures—which cost an incredible amount of money—for a health outcome that was hopeless. And the fact that the mother was not paying for these treatments really rankled the administrator who said the resources should be used for a child who had a better shot at thriving.

That day the discussion was occurring in a very economically diverse group of people. A young mother raised her hand and said that she had "been there"— that she was one of "those mothers" and that the health providers didn't under- stand that faith in God can override medical treatment: "Who is the hospital to say who God will heal that day? That baby is my child and a child of God."

Everyone wants as many babies as possible to survive and thrive. When this doesn't seem to be happening, we use our own knowledge and experiences to mitigate the situation. We hope that the mother who shared her pain had someone at that hospital who could understand and had a relationship of mutual respect with her and her family. There is no substitute for relationship and knowing that your view is heard, even if the chances of survival are minimal.

A nurse mentioned that some healthcare professionals seemed to have an almost unconscious reaction to mothers of different economic classes in the NICU. What if some of your colleagues had the following reactions?

If the mother of a NICU baby appears to be at least middle-class and is well-dressed—and if the family understands the middle-class hidden rules of decorum and communication, can complete paperwork, and knows which questions to ask and the best time to do so—it is assumed that "something happened" and that the mother had completed appropriate perinatal preventive treatment, did not smoke, drink, use drugs, or make other poor decisions that compromised the pregnancy.

The professional went on to say she had seen a different discussion about the mother who appears to be from poverty. There was likely to be less generosity in assigning good choices to the mother and family. In this case, the discussion tended to be focused on the poor choices of the under-resourced mother; chances are the mother smoked or drank during the pregnancy.

The reader can decide if this healthcare provider was accurate in her perceptions about the different ways some staff members reacted to the economic class of the patient. There may be a connection between the way one perceives a patient and the care that patient is given—or not given. It is the premise of the authors of this book that there is a correlation between the lenses we use, the relationships we establish, and the care that ultimately is provided.

Here is where knowledge of the Poverty Research Continuum (see Appendix D) is critical—if we understand that a person's choices and behaviors are only one cause of that person's poverty and circumstances, it helps us remember that poverty is multifaceted and complex. This wider view also helps us see that individual differently.

Think of a time when you may have heard comments that caused you to pause or perhaps caught you off guard.

- Maybe it was the first time you made rounds after a young man had been admitted to your floor with a diagnosis of AIDS. Do you recall the conversations?

- Have you ever taken care of a woman who was been the victim of domestic violence? What comments did you hear when her husband or partner came to the hospital to visit and insisted on taking her home?

- What comments have you heard when a morbidly obese patient comes to the ER and asks for some food during transfer to a room? Do you have favorite names for certain groups of patients, such as "frequent flyers"?

- What comments have you heard in the last week that caught your attention? How might the individual perspectives and attitudes from which those comments were made affect, consciously or subconsciously, the relationships between providers and patients?

- How might the way a person "hears" a statement affect the relationship?

- To what extent does the quality of the relationship with the patient affect treatment?

This is the business case for having a lens to clearly perceive the impact of economic class on collective efficacy. Using the Bridges lens—as well as other models to understand the psychosocial aspects of patients outside the dominant culture and economic experience of most Americans—will positively impact both cost and value.

SOCIAL CAPITAL AND GETTING AHEAD IN A JUST-GETTIN'-BY WORLD

There are different measures of poverty, one being the percentage of households or individuals under the federal poverty line (FPL), and another is the percentage of households within 198% of the FPL. The standard for a sustainable income in the U.S. is 200% above the FPL. When you combine these data for both measure of poverty, it has become the norm for most cities and counties in the U.S. to have many of their households in poverty.

Social factors and environments—such as education, income, and community—influence our lives and have direct and significant implications on health status and health outcomes. Within this research there is a strong causal link between environment and personal choice. If the goal is reduce risk and risk behaviors, the approach must include a model that addresses both individual assets, as well as environmental change.

There is not one generally accepted definition adopted by researchers for the concept of social capital. A working definition, however, is that social capital pertains to the value of social networks—bonding similar people and bridging between diverse people.[66] Inglehart's definition is aligned with the focus of the *Bridges Out of Poverty* book. Inglehart defines social capital as "a culture of trust and tolerance, in which extensive networks of voluntary associations emerge."[67] For more information, please see *www.socialcapitalresearch.com*.

Robert Putnam breaks support systems or social capital into two categories: bonding and bridging. In terms of relationships of mutual respect with patients and clients, there is no doubt that Putnam would qualify the nature of these relationships as bridging social capital. Bonding social capital involves those people within support systems that help one "get by" while one's bridging social capital helps one "get ahead."[68]

Bonding social capital can be positive or negative; Putnam gives such examples as the Ku Klux Klan or a street gang as bonding social capital that may have a negative impact on others, as well as those within the group.[69] Bonding social capital may be positive in one aspect and negative in another, e.g.: "My dad is not supportive of me quitting smoking. I think it's because he smokes too. But he's really good about watching my boy so I can go to my evening courses." In behavioral health (specifically addictions), a recurring pattern emerges. The primary relationships—partner, spouse—may not be overly supportive of an alcoholic in the recovery process; they may actually pull the addict away from working toward sobriety. Bonding social capital is complex. Putnam's description of bonding social capital is that it is more beneficial when it is "thick"—the more bonding social capital, the more positive impact it is likely to have on individuals, families, and the community.[70]

Bridging social capital can be very effective even when it is "thin." One person can make a huge impact. If you received a call from Bill Gates of Microsoft because he wanted to consult with you on matters of health and wellness, that would be paramount to your future success and the success of your research and

> **The power of "one" in terms of bridging social capital is significant.**

practice. The power of "one" in terms of bridging social capital is significant. Notice in the following diagram that bonding social capital is represented as "thick"—with each small circle representing an individual who assists with day-to-day resources, such as food, childcare, transportation, etc. There is only one larger circle depicted in bridging social capital, not that it must be limited to one, but to illustrate, as noted, that it can be useful even if "thin."

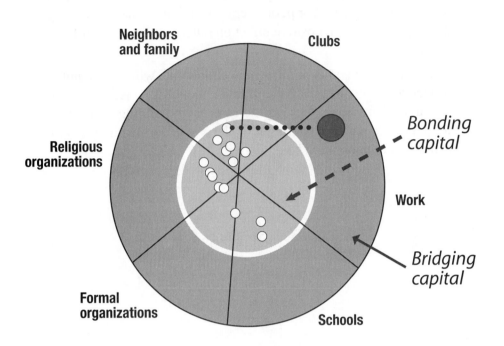

Source: *Getting Ahead in a Just-Gettin'-By World;* adapted
by P. E. DeVol, based on R. Putnam's concepts.

QUESTIONS FOR REFLECTION

1. With which groups of patients or clients do you feel most comfortable?
   What might be the reasons for that?

2. Why do patients and clients in poverty respond to relationship and trust
   even more than someone in a financially stable or financially abundant
   environment? In your organization or institution, how do you currently
   address this?

3. How might engaging individuals in poverty at the decision-making table
   impact relationships with patients and clients who are involved in your
   practice or facility?

4. To what extent is your practice or facility centered on relationships or on outcomes? How could value for cost be increased if relationships were primary when working with groups at higher risk of noncompliance and/or poor overall health outcomes? How might this approach have a positive effect on outcomes, as it did at Ellis Medicine?

5. It will take time and commitment to collaborate with community service agencies to assist patients and clients with missing external resources. How could these agencies assist in building social capital for patients/clients? What might be the payoff for the time spent in increasing collaboration?

CHAPTER SEVEN

FOUR CASE STUDIES

The following case studies may remind you of patients, family members, friends, or someone you know. A set of questions follows each case study, and each one is debriefed. These case studies also are designed for discussion.

The first three case studies in this chapter look at individuals and their resources. The last one deals with institutions and communities.

CASE STUDY #3—RANDY'S FAMILY

Randy came from a middle-class household until his father died when he was 6. Randy was one of six children. Randy's father was an alcoholic and a smoker and died of lung emphysema. The family was thrust into "situational" poverty because his mother didn't work outside the home. There was no money for dentists and almost none for healthcare. His mother, Shelly, smoked also. Food was home-cooked and good—beans, cornbread, meat, sandwiches. There were very few fresh vegetables or fresh fruit; they were simply too expensive. The plot of land they lived on was too small for a garden. There were no sports or athletic activities but it was in a rural area so the children spent a great deal of time outdoors, in the woods, and running and playing.

For weekend entertainment, they often watched the neighbor man come home from the bar, drunk and violent. As he shuffled toward his house, he would start yelling and throwing his empty whiskey or beer bottles against the house or through the front window to announce his arrival. The neighbor's children would run out the back door along with their mother. When all was quiet, the neighbor's children and wife would come back. The next morning, the hung-over neighbor would be replacing the broken glass. Randy and his siblings called it "Friday night at the fights!"

Randy started smoking when he was 12. All the children started drinking coffee at a very young age. There were no soft drinks in the home; they cost too much. There was no drinking in the home; booze also cost too much. All of Randy's five siblings smoked—as teens and as adults. His older brother, Greg, went to Vietnam at 18 and came back at 22 with an addiction to heroin, cocaine, and alcohol.

Visits to the doctor or the ER were rare and only in an emergency. The dentist was out of the question. Transportation wasn't available; the family's only car was sold for cash after Dad's death. Furthermore, in this high-poverty neighborhood, "real men" didn't go to the doctor. If you were in pain, you drank. If you were uncomfortable, you didn't talk about it. You could be grouchy and unpleasant, but you didn't complain. Counseling was only for "wimps."

When Randy's father died, there was no counseling. He was dead. There was no point in talking about it. And furthermore, Randy's mother was glad that he was dead because he was so difficult at the end of his illness, and there was no support for her.

When Randy was 22, he married Susan, from middle class, and her ideas about health were very different from what he had grown up with. She wanted balanced meals that weren't fried. She bought fresh fruit and raised some vegetables. For the most part, Randy refused to eat them. And she wanted to keep her weight healthy. In fact, one of the men in the neighborhood said to Randy, "That girl ain't got no love handles." He meant that she didn't have enough fat to "get a handle" on her. Almost all the women in Randy's neighborhood were overweight. The men even seemed to prefer that the women be on the heavy side.

Randy's mother got an abscessed breast because she was diabetic and wouldn't address the fact. Randy found out and forced her to go to the doctor. Shelly said to him that Bill, her second husband and Randy's stepfather, didn't want "no doctor lookin' at her body." But Randy was persistent. She finally went and admitted she had diabetes—and started taking medicine for it. However, she wouldn't take the medicine the way it was prescribed because she didn't "like the doctor."

As she aged, Randy's mother became very religious and very fatalistic. She told Susan, "When it's my time to die, it's my time to die." Susan asked her why God gave her a brain if she wasn't going to use it. And so periodically, usually about twice a year, Shelly would end up in the hospital because of the unpredictability of her medications and eating habits.

The young doctor who was assigned to Shelly was the one she didn't like. So as he came into the room, she would say very loudly, "There's that doctor I don't like! Did they send you in here again?" Not knowing how to handle her, the doctor would rush through his time, barely look at her, and get out as fast as he could. And so, there was virtually no communication with the doctor.

As Randy grew older, he continued to smoke—and every day for lunch had a cheeseburger and fries. He didn't exercise; he just worked hard (his idea of exercise). Randy's favorite food groups were cheese, meat, and potatoes. Sometimes beans. Occasionally green beans. And bread. Lots of bread. He didn't drink because of the family history of alcoholism. He would say, "If I start drinkin', I might not be able to stop. So I ain't gonna start."

Randy's older brother, Greg, who had been in Vietnam, came back addicted to both opiates and alcohol. He didn't have his brother's self-discipline in relation to alcohol. His first marriage was quite violent; he nearly killed his first wife twice. After the second attempt, he was put into a psychiatric institution for several weeks. He soon conned the psychiatrist into believing that he was fine—and so was released. He smoked both marijuana and cigarettes and developed a nasty cough.

In and out of jail several times, Greg let his health take a "back seat" to daily living. He was fastidious about his personal appearance but not his health. He didn't exercise, though (like Randy) he usually worked hard as a manual laborer. He died in jail at the age of 60 from cancer, lung, and liver complications. During Greg's six decades on earth he seldom saw a doctor.

Randy's mother died in the hospital of diabetes complications at the age of 75.

About 30 years into Susan and Randy's marriage, Randy (like Greg) developed a hacking cough one winter. It went on for months. Susan begged, pushed, and finally persuaded her husband to see a doctor. When Randy returned home, she asked him what the doctor said. Randy replied, "I have good news and bad news." Susan asked what it was. He said, "Well the good news is that I'm the healthiest man the doctor has seen in months. And the bad news is that it will *take me months* to pay his bill!" And that pretty much summed up Randy's view of doctors and medicine.

Randy died seven years later at the age of 59 of a heart attack. He was dead on arrival at the hospital.

Soon after her husband's death, Susan signed up for a "boutique" doctor for a fee of $1500 membership. The doctor was limited to 600 patients (total) and gave his cell phone number to Susan. He told her that if she had a medical issue outside of office hours to call him on the cell phone and not to go to the emergency room but call him first. He would decide the best care for the medical issue.

Susan went to him once a year for a full physical, and the doctor spent about an hour with her, going over the blood tests and additional tests and data. He gave Susan an inventory for depression, food habits, sexual habits, exercise patterns, as well as a hearing test and a breathing test. Susan knew the name of his receptionist and, at Christmas, she bought the receptionist a bottle of wine. Susan understood that the relationship with the receptionist was critical in maintaining a good working relationship with her doctor.

Susan's mother and father were still alive at 88 and 91 and lived in a rural area in another state. Every day one of their sons would check on them to see how they were doing. Susan's father was diabetic, had congestive heart failure, a replaced hip and knee, and numbness in his fingers and toes. Susan's mother had a knee-replacement surgery that went badly. Both of Susan's parents had unusually clear minds for people their age, but their bodies were frail. At least once a week, one or both of them went to see a doctor. The waits in the waiting room were long—two or three hours. Because they were both on Medicare and had supplemental insurance, finding a doctor who would take them in a rural area wasn't easy, and the choices were limited.

One doctor prescribed oxygen to be taken by Susan's father. He would cooperate with the visiting nurse when she came and put on the apparatus, but after she left he would take it back off. Susan's mother tried (unsuccessfully) to get the oxygen discontinued because, to her, there were too many oxygen tanks sitting around.

After Susan's mother got sick and went to the hospital for three weeks, she came home very weak. Her granddaughter came twice a week to clean the house and do the laundry. The preparation and care of food became quite an issue in the household. The children and grandchildren knew not to eat what was in the refrigerator because no one was sure how long it had been there. But because the sons checked in with them every day, they were monitored daily.

QUESTIONS

1. What resources were available in this situation? Using a scale of 1–3, rate the resources of each individual.

Resource	Randy	Greg (his brother)	Shelly (their mother)	Susan
Financial				
Emotional				
Mental/cognitive				
Spiritual (future story)				
Physical				

continued on next page

continued from previous page

Resource	Randy	Greg (his brother)	Shelly (their mother)	Susan
Support systems				
Relationships/ role models				
Knowledge of hidden rules				
Language/ formal register				

2. Which of these research bases most impacted the healthcare delivery outcomes? Why?

Access	Availability	Cost	Quality	Efficacy	Communication

3. What could have been done differently to enhance the outcomes?

4. Also answer questions 1–3 about Susan's parents.

ADDITIONAL QUESTION AND DEBRIEFING

1. To what extent did Randy change the health outcomes of his mother?

CASE STUDY #4—JAMES SMITH

James Smith is a 62-year-old homeless Vietnam-era veteran. Married at 19, he returned from Vietnam to a wife and child. Although described as a happy-go-lucky kid and teenager prior to his six years in the service, upon returning, his personality changed to very quiet and serious. He had difficulty sleeping, though he rarely complained. After drinking one or two six packs of beer most evenings, James managed to go to work daily. At work or at home, he smoked cigarettes constantly. He completed college and joined an accounting firm.

One day James came home to learn that his wife had moved out, taking their son. That week he was served with divorce papers. His family said he was never the same after that. He was 35 years old. Within a year, he lost his job. He never seemed to work at a "real job" after that. He moved in with his mother.

She died a year later. When his mother's house was sold, he got in a car, and his sister didn't know where he went. He called her on her birthday.

James grew up in a traditional two-parent family with a younger sister; they lived in a working-class neighborhood. His father was a mechanic at the local garage. His mother was a stay-at-home mom who sometimes did a little sewing for people to make extra money. James played baseball, was popular at school, and was voted the most popular male in his high school.

The family attended a neighborhood church, and he was baptized when he was 10. After Vietnam, he insisted he was an atheist, much to his mother's dismay. His father died from a heart attack when James was 30. He married his childhood sweetheart after he was drafted to go to Vietnam.

James is an alcoholic, frequently smokes marijuana, and says he isn't a "druggie" because he doesn't "do coke or heroin." He says he smokes "weed" so he can sleep. James adds that he can still hear gunshots and his buddies yelling whenever he's almost asleep. When he wakes up, he can feel his heart racing. He was arrested once for drunk and disorderly conduct. James has his "drinking buddies." Most of them also are homeless.

James smokes as many regular cigarettes as he can buy or beg. He has experienced several blackouts and was brought to the hospital after being mugged and beaten up. Since admission, he was prescribed medication for sleep and treated for *delirium tremens* (DTs). He is expected to make a full recovery from pneumonia. He told the social worker he won't ask his sister if he can live with her because she and her husband kicked him out for smoking weed the last time he "visited." He also doesn't want to go to "one of those homes." He has been in rehab before, and it was OK, but he has no interest in going back. He has repeatedly stated he doesn't intend to quit smoking or drinking.

Currently James lives in a rooming house and pays $375 a month. His most recent "girlfriend" kicked him out of her house several months ago. He is a "service-connected veteran"; there is a Veterans Administration (VA) Hospital in the community where he now lives. He has no car. His driver's license has been suspended since his last DUI (driving under the influence). He receives approximately $1250 a month from different sources. He is described as having a charming personality when he is sober. He believes God has "given up on him." James likes to read. Because of his reading habits and the way he speaks, his drinking buddies call him "the professor."

James doesn't like going to the VA for clinic appointments. He says they make him wait too long. His favorite doctor moved, and he doesn't like the one to whom he is currently assigned.

The city in which James lives is a large urban area. It comprises 3,700 square miles and has a population of 1 million residents. Thirty-seven percent of the population is Hispanic, 37% black, 16% is white non-Hispanic, and 9% is Asian-Pacific Islander. About 55% of the population has a high school diploma or more, while 18% has a bachelor's degree or more.

Measured by the latest employment numbers, the leading industries are logistics and professional and business services. The "new economy" is largely technology-driven, very limited, and includes bio-medical and environmental technology. Local officials are trying to build a larger manufacturing presence. There are multiple blighted areas, and the tax base has decreased as people have moved to suburban areas. Housing prices are reasonable compared with nearby communities. Higher and specialized education, as well as career colleges, are available. Recreational opportunities include lake activities.

QUESTIONS

1. What are James' resources? Using a scale of 1–3, assess James' resources.

Resource	James
Financial	
Emotional	
Mental/cognitive	
Spiritual (future story)	
Physical	
Support systems	

continued on next page

continued from previous page

Resource	James
Relationships/ role models	
Knowledge of hidden rules	
Language/ formal register	

2. Which of these research bases most impacted the healthcare delivery outcomes? Why?

Access	Availability	Cost	Quality	Efficacy	Communication

3. What could have been done differently to enhance the outcomes?

ADDITIONAL QUESTIONS AND DEBRIEFING

1. How might self-efficacy analysis be applied in this case?

2. In what type of environment does James currently find himself?

3. The next time James shows up at the hospital, how will he be greeted by the medical personnel?

4. If the analysis shows that James is not prepared to do the level of intensive work required to change in the traditional rehab setting, who is willing to say that he may be better served to undergo treatment at a later date? In other words, while efforts can be made to increase James' motivation for treatment, might he and others with a similar presentation and history be advised "to consider treatment on some future occasion when concerns are greater than by failure through half-hearted attempts, which only strengthens their belief in the futility of efforts at personal change"?[71]

CASE STUDY #5—DIABETES: THE WEAVER FAMILY

J. D. and Elvira Weaver live on 50 acres of land in rural Tennessee that has been in the family for three to four generations. The trees have been harvested and not replanted, and the farm is not worth much because it's in the heart of a poverty-stricken part of the state in what seems like the middle of nowhere. However, it provides a home for 78-year-old J. D., 79-year-old Elvira (J. D.'s second wife), their 31-year-old daughter Mary Sue and her 13-year-old daughter Tammy Lynn.

Mr. Weaver's first wife passed away many years ago; they had two daughters and one son together. Elvira brought one daughter, now an adult, into the marriage and Mary Sue is the child of her marriage to J. D. All the other children took flight from the farm as soon as they were old enough, moving to faraway states. As the youngest, almost a generation apart from her stepsiblings, Mary Sue was never able to escape.

Mr. and Mrs. Weaver are on Medicaid and Medicare. Mary Sue's young husband is deployed in the U.S. military overseas. Following a recent accident, Tammy Lynn has TNCare Medicaid coverage. Three months ago, she was thrown from one of the horses on the farm when it was startled by a snake. She suffered a broken pelvis and right femur. She was hospitalized for almost three months in the nearest tertiary-care hospital, a three-hour drive from their home.

Tammy recently came back home and has been assigned to a home health nurse, Kathy Nardis, RN, and today is nurse Nardis' first visit to assess Tammy Lynn's progress and the conditions in the home. Upon arrival, having taken that same three-hour drive, nurse Nardis remarked to Mary Sue that she had not expected the 10-mile journey from the highway, followed by a two-mile, bumpy drive from the road where the Weavers' mailbox is located. She was, however, impressed with the size and bounty of the vegetable garden, the fruit trees, a few cows, chickens, and the two horses she saw on the property.

Mary Sue told nurse Nardis that going to the only primary physician in the area took a full day—made all the worse because she didn't like the doctor, plus the waiting room was always "wall to wall" full. Getting another PCP (primary care provider) would mean traveling even farther.

The home is a fairly large wooden farm house in much need of painting and repair. The inside of the house was clean, although it seems that nothing has ever been thrown away. The nurse noticed that Mary Sue is clearly the spokesperson and main caregiver for the family. Mr. Weaver repeatedly interrupted their conversation with requests for attention and pointedly ignored nurse Nardis.

Nurse Nardis began her assessment by asking about the health of Tammy's grandfather. Mr. Weaver is a morbidly obese diabetic. The nurse learned that he was initially treated with oral medication. His blood sugar was continually out of control, so he was placed on insulin injections two times a day, with sliding-scale insulin to cover each meal. His blood sugars continue to run in the 300s every day. Mary Sue has learned to give the insulin shots and perform the blood tests.

Sensing where the conversation might be going, Mary Sue suddenly said,

> We aren't happy with the prescriptions from the doctor and don't much believe in medicine anyway. So I let Daddy take his home remedies and only use what I have to from the drugs prescribed by the doctor. When something goes wrong and we call the doctor's office, it can take days for them to get back with us. When we go in to the office, they try to stuff a whole lot of information down our throats at one time, and I don't understand half of what they're saying anyway. So I just tune them out. The same thing happens if I try to talk to them on the phone.

Nurse Nardis asked Mr. Weaver, "How can we work together to bring your blood sugar down and not have to increase your meds?" His response: "I'm an old man, I love to eat, and it's too late for me to change." Looking at his medications, nurse Nardis saw that he was being treated with two prescriptions for dyslipidemia (high cholesterol) and a drug specific to high triglycerides.

Using the plates in the house to show Mary Sue what she means by portion size, nurse Nardis instructed her to make the small change of giving Mr. Weaver exactly what he likes to eat but in much smaller portions. The nurse asked Mr. Weaver if he would go along with this plan, and he agreed, saying, "It doesn't take much to get me full anyway."

While surveying and checking the kitchen, nurse Nardis noticed a large amount of packaged chips, candy, nuts, and cookies. Although the Weavers grow quite a bit of their own food and slaughter chickens and the occasional cow, Mary Sue said the closest thing to a grocery store is the Dollar Store in town, and they stock up on snacks there.

When nurse Nardis inquired about other diseases in the family, Mary Sue, who looks 20 years older than her 31 years, replied, "We all have diabetes, and all the women are fat like my daddy." Wife #1 didn't have diabetes, although the current Mrs. Weaver does.

Continuing with the history taking, the nurse discovered that Mr. Weaver smokes a pack of non-filtered cigarettes a day, and both women chew tobacco. Mary Sue said that "chewing ain't as dangerous as smoking." Nurse Nardis asked for a hand mirror and proceeded to gently teach Mary Sue and Mrs. Weaver how to look inside the mouth cavity and observe the actual darkening of the mucosa—and how to check for lesions in the mouth and under the tongue. She warned them that cancerous lesions in the mouth may not be painful and thus can easily be missed. They both looked amazed and seemed to appreciate what they were seeing and learning!

Warming up to nurse Nardis, Mary Sue told her about the "lumps" on Mr. Weaver's back and legs. She said she had called the insurance company's "Nurse Call Line" several months back to ask what to do about them and was told to take him to a doctor. "As usual," she said, "the call was a disaster because they tried to make me think I was stupid and acted like they couldn't understand what I was saying."

In the past she had received calls from the insurance company to follow up on Mr. Weaver's diabetes. Those calls also were very unproductive and left her feeling like she wasn't doing enough or was stupid. She said, "They tried to sound nice and sweet, but I could tell they didn't mean it. They act like I should know what to do, and I don't!" She said she didn't follow the instructions to take her father to the PCP because it was a three-hour drive each way, and she had homeschooling and the farm to take care of. She had decided to "just squeeze them herself and drain the pus out." After that, they just seemed to spread and come right back.

Nurse Nardis took a look and suspected they were MRSA (methicillin-resistant staph aureus) lesions based on the history of reoccurrence and the malodorous pus. Mary Sue was instructed by nurse Nardis to contact her PCP, describe the "lumps," and ask for antibiotics, explaining that she couldn't come in now because of Tammy's condition.

At this point, Mary Sue talked about how she was taking care of mother, father, and her own child and was unable to keep her own diabetes under control. Her only pleasure lately is in food, she admitted. Mrs. Weaver has been diagnosed with diabetes and refuses to take any medications because she doesn't trust the medicines or the doctors and is "taking care of it herself with diet." However, she too is morbidly obese. There are lots of cousins in the area, but the family avoids asking them for help because they don't want them putting claims on the land if something happens to Mr. Weaver. In addition, Mr. Weaver has become more and more forgetful and paranoid the past few years.

Finally getting to Tammy Lynn, the nurse was very concerned about the possibility of diabetes. Mary Sue said that Tammy had developed breasts very quickly but at 13, unlike her at that age, she still hadn't started her menses. This had never come up during Tammy's three-month stay in the hospital. Mary Sue said that was probably because during the hospital stay she had been able to visit her daughter just once a week because of the distance, the money, and having to take care of the senior Weavers and the farm. To visit the hospital even that often, she had grudgingly asked one of the cousins to stay while she was gone, but she didn't want them there too long. Mary Sue clearly felt bad about this and said the only way she got through that experience—and every day now—was by "constantly praying to the good Lord for strength to carry on."

Mary Sue then confided to nurse Nardis that her dream was to help Tammy Lynn get off the farm. Her parents went only to eighth grade, and she was the child of their old age; she had been fortunate to barely finish high school. Mary Sue said she could get food stamps now that Tammy had TNCare but was too proud to do so—and anyway, she would have to drive three hours to the city to use them and avoid being seen. Otherwise, Tammy seemed to be doing fine, except that she wasn't doing the prescribed exercises and sat snacking in front of the television all day.

What nurse Nardis expected to be a one-hour home visit turned into a three-hour consultation for the entire family. The nurse left with a four-part plan: Increase the frequency of home visits, include the entire family in the visits, get social services involved for everybody, and get a personal support worker to help Mary Sue with Tammy and Mr. Weaver.

Nurse Nardis felt sure there was more she needed to do, but she was just too tired to think about it anymore. She still had a long drive ahead of her.

QUESTIONS

1. What are the resources that Mary Sue and Tammy have? Using a scale of 1–3, rate the resources of each individual.

Resource	Mary Sue	Tammy
Financial		
Emotional		
Mental/cognitive		
Spiritual (future story)		
Physical		
Support systems		
Relationships/ role models		
Knowledge of hidden rules		
Language/ formal register		

3. Which of these research bases most impacted the healthcare delivery outcomes? Why?

Access	Availability	Cost	Quality	Efficacy	Communication

4. What could have been done differently to enhance the outcomes?

ADDITIONAL QUESTIONS AND DEBRIEFING

1. Based on the results, what else would you do for the Weavers? How might this family's strengths be better leveraged to their advantage?

2. What desirable skills did nurse Nardis demonstrate in her visit with the Weavers? What will it take for her interventions to stick?

3. In what ways did the insurance company's efforts to communicate and manage Mr. Weaver's care fall short—and how could they be improved?

4. How do issues of access, availability, cost, efficacy, communication, and quality show up in a situation of rural generational poverty and chronic disease? Is there a significant variable unlike what might appear in urban incidence?

5. How might the same conditions—an accident, emergency care, and diabetes—have presented and been handled in a rural *wealthy* family?

INSTITUTIONAL CASE STUDY

CASE STUDY #6—IMPACT OF POLICIES

The state of Tennessee has two major safety-net hospitals, which also may be public. They are the places prepared and inspected when the president of the United States travels in the vicinity. Should the president be injured, this is where he/she will go. The Tennessee hospitals are in the state's capital, Nashville, and in the southwestern corner of the state, Memphis.

The Memphis hospital is The Regional Medical Center of Memphis (The MED). The MED is bordered by Mississippi and Arkansas and is an academic medical center in partnership with the University of Tennessee in the training of physicians. In fact, the care of patients had been provided through this symbiotic relationship for 180 years. As a safety-net hospital, it has long offered the highest credentialed categories of Centers of Excellence serving the Mid-South.

These Centers of Excellence include a Level III Trauma Center, the oldest, high-level Newborn Center and NICU (neonatal intensive care unit), a Burn Center and a high-risk Obstetrics Center. It also boasted one of the largest outpatient clinics in the state, serving every specialty and sub-specialty imaginable. Children were seen at the children's hospital across the street, which was not part of The MED.

In 1993 the volume of births at The MED reached an impressive 10,000. While The MED seemed to have cornered the market for births, it still averaged $20 million to $26 million in uncompensated care annually. This had only recently begun to be partially mitigated by an expansion of Medicaid funding for women and children, which used a mix of provider donations and taxes to draw down federal matching funds. Indigent care is not mandated for any public or private entity beyond emergent care.

In a city with a high crime and poverty rate, the emergency room and trauma center of The MED would often find themselves on what was called "divergence" because it was known that this was the first place to bring what was known in the medical community as "the knife and gun club." Knife wounds would end up in The MED emergency room and gunshot wounds in the trauma center. When both of these were full to overflowing—and there were no more rooms in which to admit patients—"divergence" meant that The MED could legally turn patients away from the ER or trauma center if they arrived by ambulance.

The president and CEO of The MED and select members of her staff were very active at both the state and national level in lobbying and advancing dialogue to create even more relief from the burden of disproportionately caring for the Medicaid population, the poor in general, and the victims and perpetrators of crime within this large urban community with a population of well-documented, economically disparate African Americans. The city's population was nearly 60% African American.

It also should be noted that this is the city where the Rev. Dr. Martin Luther King, Jr. was killed in 1968, and the city still carried the psychological burden of this event and a great deal of history not uncommon to the segregated South. In 1993 the Clinton Administration and Hillary Rodham Clinton, specifically, took on healthcare reform as a key initiative. Eventually, obtaining a waiver under Section 1115 of the Social Security Act, The MED made many changes to allow for much-needed expansion of care, payments, and the introduction of managed care to this population of women, children, and SSI (supplemental security income) beneficiaries. It was an outstanding program that provided coverage to the uninsured, as well as to people with medical conditions that previously made them uninsurable. Since there was no upper-income limit, anyone over the poverty line could pay premiums on a sliding scale based on ability to pay.

While administrators and staff at The MED and the medical school were excited about these outcomes, there was a significant and perverse downside. All of this would take place in a managed-care environment with mandatory open enrollment for the beneficiaries. Enter choice. The president and CEO of The MED made this statement at the time:

> It does not matter that we have provided excellent care to people in generational poverty for decades. We will see an exodus of patients analogous to what happened in Memphis on the day that black folk learned that we could ride the city buses and sit wherever we wanted to. Many people took the bus on that day to simply experience the power of choice. Having ridden the bus to and from high school, always sitting in the rear of the bus, I would have been one of those people who exercised my choice to sit in the front on that day. The seats were not better, but they were different![72]

We knew that our most threatened market would be in the maternity hospital. The length of stay and the risk are not as high in that population, and the reimbursement was very competitive. Yet we knew that the less attractive subsets of diagnoses would still end up with us, and our acuity rates would increase.

The MED quickly formed an alliance with the university, as this state school's physician training program could be adversely affected by a drop in its patient population, which was almost exclusively at The MED. We lobbied the governor and met *ad infinitum* with his administration to create some form of set-aside enrollments to protect the university and our own bottom line. The university and the hospital jointly formed a managed-care organization (MCO). This was a significant step in collaboration between the two.

At the same time, however, other MCOs were rapidly forming around the state and galvanized to descend on Memphis as soon as open enrollment began. Many of these groups were very savvy when it came to marketing to people in generational poverty. Their methods covered lots of giveaways and neighborhood partying.

With only a year to plan and execute a strategy for survival in this new model, up until the very last minute, it was thought that The MED would receive some assistance from the state to protect our market share. This was not to be. Within two years of implementation, the institution saw a 20% decrease in births, a rise in acuity, and a battle for funds on a field intended to be more level. The

TennCare program was itself very successful. It quickly expanded coverage from 900,000 to 1.4 million, achieved the second lowest per-enrollee costs in the country and saved the state upwards of $2 billion in its first six years.

The MED, however, was faced with learning to live in an environment where there was competition for a previously unattractive market. The TennCare program later developed major challenges around funding that eventually led to near collapse in 2002. In mid-2005, the state terminated coverage for all uninsured and uninsurable adults, but it maintained some coverage for uninsured children.

There have been many more changes leading into the present. The MED has survived via new and increasingly creative funding means—and will continue to survive due, in large part, to its strong commitment to its mission.

QUESTIONS AND DEBRIEFING

1. How did legislative policy lose its intentionality at implementation in relationship to institutional efficacy?

2. How is collective efficacy influenced by political necessity and vice versa?

3. How is it that collective efficacy trumped years of failed self-efficacy in the face of an opportunity of unexpected choice?

4. As funding evolves under the Patient Protection and Affordable Care Act (ACA)—with future changes yet to be determined—how do safety-net hospitals compete to become hospitals of choice?

5. For safety-net hospitals perceived as the choice of "last resort," what can be done to cultivate deeper relationships of respect with patients?

6. What might the effect be of the closure of a public safety-net hospital in your community?

7. How does "choice" impact patient satisfaction or perception of care?

8. How are other institutions and providers affected, as patients make different choices?

9. What lessons have we learned from the closure of public safety-net hospitals?

10. Where are the opportunities to build community efficacy before a safety-net hospital has to close? During a closure process? After a closure?

CONCLUSION

If positive health outcomes are to be realized for individuals in poverty, if health and healthcare disparities are to be impacted, a broader brush of strategies is necessary. ***The focus must move away from merely improving services to improving environments.*** The more the health and healthcare sectors understand this imperative, the more likely they will be to change policies and praxis to truly improve the health of people in poverty, to increase efficacy, and to lower the costs of healthcare.

Indeed, the ultimate long-term goal must not be just providing great services to individuals in poverty, but at the community and policy level to move toward economic stability.

If poverty is a contributing factor to the stress that causes health disparities, then poverty must be reduced and even eradicated in order to reduce disparities. No health organization has the power to do this singlehandedly, of course, just as no sector has the power to do this in isolation. Impacting environments is possible through collective-impact models of shared responsibility, data collection, and common goals and objectives across all sectors.[73]

The Bridges Out of Poverty structures that support this type of initiative are fourfold:

1. Getting Ahead in a Just-Gettin'-By World.[74] For more information, please visit *www.gettingaheadnetwork.com*. Getting Ahead provides individuals in poverty with tools to become involved in building resources for their own lives, as well as assisting at the decision-making tables of institutions and the community.

2. The development of a Bridges Steering Committee, built on the collective-impact model of collaborative change, which includes individuals in poverty at the collaboration table. For more information, please visit *www.ahaprocess.com* where there are links to the websites of established Bridges Communities having a positive impact on stabilizing environments and individuals. Philip DeVol's book *Bridges to Sustainable Communities*[75] details the ways in which many communities already have been moving toward community sustainability using the Bridges lens.

3. Bridges Out of Poverty training within every community sector (both public and private) and with citizens not associated with any service-provider system. For more information, please visit *www.ahaprocess. com*.

4. Bridges to Health and Healthcare training within healthcare institutions and health agencies. This training will (a) enhance awareness among leadership and staff of the impact of economic class and (b) create a common language for strategy development and solutions. This training can significantly enhance or even replace many of the time-consuming and cumbersome models currently being used to address regulatory and accreditation mandates for change. For more information, please visit *www.ahaprocess.com*.

Some policymakers and community advocates have shifted away from "provider centered" models of assisting those in poverty toward a community-based, social-capital model that literally builds relationship and social cohesion. This moves the playing field to "one on one," which we know will always be part of the human experience.

In such social-capital models, individuals who have sustainability engage in a long-term bridging social capital model with checks and balances, with mutual growth between allies (persons with sustainability) and the individual who is in poverty. Provider-centered models rely on agencies to improve the living standards of those in poverty, but the question is: To what extent will this result in a sustainable income and lifestyle for the individual in poverty?

To further personalize the issue, we can ask ourselves these additional questions:

> *Is it I? What policies are in place in my institution, what biases do I hold, what practices have I adopted, what insensitivities do I display that may be presenting a barrier to the health of people in poverty?*

To be sure, these questions are equally important with regard to all at-risk and vulnerable individuals, not just those in poverty.

Innovations in poverty reduction are happening through community collective impact rather than isolated impact where institutions strategize solely within the institution to achieve certain outcomes. The emerging concept of poverty reduction is the increased focus on relationships—building bridging social capital for individuals in poverty who typically don't have access to the professional social networks that help to build sustainability.

Our view is that the larger goals of health and wellness for individuals within all populations are directly linked to increased institutional sustainability, the intentional design of social cohesion and improving community environments. Individual, institutional, and community sustainability will never be realized without relationships—interactions that embed personal growth—and without bridging social capital.

> ## *"Relationship is a sledgehammer that obliterates every societal difference."*
>
> –Robert Sapolsky[76]

The concepts explored in this book can work (to use a military term) as a "force multiplier" for any model truly created to improve health outcomes. As Paul Starr notes in *The Social Transformation of American Medicine,* "History does not provide any answers about what should be done."[77]

In this book we have offered, for your consideration, a different and unique lens through which to look at health and healthcare—as a complement to the view you currently hold. We trust there can be a synergistic result as both views are blended. Perhaps finding and implementing the Holy Grail of efficacious healthcare is possible after all.

APPENDIX A

PROVIDER STAKEHOLDER INTERVIEWS

In preparation for writing this book, we interviewed some of the key provider stakeholders in a large urban community in the Mid-South. The professionals interviewed are very much engaged in local, state, and national peer group activity, including research into ways to better navigate and influence the changing landscape of healthcare in America. Every single interviewee has much at stake—as a provider, payer, or consumer. We are very grateful for their input, as it has helped to inform the further development of our model for *Bridges to Health and Healthcare.*

Our conversations engaged the CEOs of billion-dollar healthcare delivery systems, educators, public health providers, insurers, consumers, and others. A list of those interviewed is found at the end of this summary.

We have included some key findings and associated comments. The interviews focused initially on the impact of the Patient Protection and Affordable Care Act (ACA) of 2010[78] on health status. It became immediately apparent that while the interviewees were concerned about the impact of ACA, changes aimed at improving quality, health status, and managing cost was a familiar and longstanding arena of struggle. Most comments took into consideration the long-term nature of the challenges and the capacity for survival regardless of the latest form of legislation. In addition, we were attempting to isolate the most significant challenges or "pains" of this stakeholder group.

KEY FINDINGS WITH COMMENTS

1. A changing model is emerging that ideally will cause patient outcomes to become more predictable.
    a. "However, we have to pursue two goals simultaneously:
        i. Following the current reimbursement model.
        ii. Finding resources to change the model for what we do while we are not paid to do that."

2. The new model must include population-based care management strategies.
    a. "We are challenged by obesity, diabetes, and multi-system conditions."
    b. "The costs of trauma- and crime-related injuries are continually rising."
    c. "A huge part of the public health budget in our community is for the provision of incarcerated individuals. What if we had a way to positively influence the health of individuals before they became the responsibility of the judicial system?"
    d. "The next great stride in prenatal care and disease prevention will take place at the level of the care of women at all stages of life—before they become child-bearing, as well as after."

3. Financial incentives *must* change. Presently, most community initiatives to improve health outcomes go straight to the bottom line.
    a. "We desperately need a framework for going upstream, for forging relationships within the community."
    b. "The biggest bang for the buck is the capacity to create new products that benefit the community *in situ*" [in its localized place or condition].

4. The search is on for new revenue streams that don't increase costs or require new brick and mortar.
    a. "Today, we are financially incentivized to satisfy our bond issuers. That means more and more brick-and-mortar projects."
    b. "It is the new piece of technology, the new test, or the new revenue-producing gadget that gets approval. We don't get paid for 'soft' care solutions."

5. A history of competition between providers is an impediment to achieving better use of limited resources and to having greater community impact in improving health status.

   a. "Fifty percent of doctors are presently aligned with hospitals, and 90% of doctors will be in the next five years."

   b. "There are no primary care docs at all in some poverty-stricken ZIP codes."

   c. "There are many community initiatives, but without a common language and understanding of the community the results are not as sustainable." (As stated in the Preface, more than 200 Bridges Communities around the world are addressing this very issue.)

   d. "It's hard for me to explain to my board of directors the financial impact of community programs that we don't get reimbursed for. We want to make a difference, but it takes money to consistently do that."

6. Key solutions to current challenges include: education and training of staff, patient satisfaction and customer service, cultural competence, technology to organize patient information, and targeted use of consultants for problem solving.

   a. "We are making multi-million-dollar investments in electronic medical records, and they are essential to reducing costs and creating better patient outcomes."

   b. "Consultancy dollars are being spent on legal issues and building delivery models that work for the future."

   c. "Strategic solutions will come from the C-suites" [top management].

   d. "Operational solutions will come from the caregivers closest to the patients."

It was clear from our interviews that the complexities of caring for individuals across economic class lines were deleteriously affecting productivity. There seemed to be no clear answers regarding how to meet the ongoing and growing demand for solutions. This conundrum was expected to be exacerbated by the influx of patients with new access and long-term multi-system conditions needing care in ways that have not been previously incentivized. Some organizations already have been spending large sums of money learning systems to improve patient satisfaction. Yet these new systems have not been producing measurable changes in resource utilization and in patient health status—or they require longer timelines for results related to health outcomes.

From our interviews, it seemed virtually unanimous that the most productive areas for change that participants can most influence are at the level of community and policy. It was believed that at the community level, change will emerge primarily through participation by all community members. At the policy level, change will emerge based largely on the type and amount of funding that policymakers offer.

One of the major stakeholders interviewed commented that the uncertainty is so great that in planning at their organization they are taking the route of "What if" scenarios and maintaining a focus on controlling, as much as possible, what goes on in their own institution. I think everyone interviewed would agree that a "Holy Grail" for healthcare would be a significant find right now! All of these helpful individuals are to be commended for their sincere and relentless efforts to address alignment—and, in some cases, realignment—of the multiple pieces of the puzzle.

Healthcare provider institutions are vital threads in the fabric of any community. These provider stakeholder interviews emphasize the disconnect between legislation, policy, and tradition on the one hand and the creation of meaningful incentives for patient-centered care on the other. In much of this book, the concepts of self-, community, institutional, and collective efficacy are defined and explored. A great deal of effort and expense is put forth every day in healthcare institutions that use a competitive model that generally does not financially reward creativity and collaboration for change. In some of the case studies you have read in this book, you have seen examples of institutional/traditional forces disrupting and even disabling well-intentioned interventions by those struggling to meet patient-care needs. Those individuals in the healthcare profession who do attempt to work creatively and collaboratively all too often find themselves bumping up against walls of rules, policies, and practices oriented principally toward "serving reimbursement" and "the cost of doing business."

Caregivers, managers, and even executives may find themselves reprimanded for being perceived as stepping outside the box in their efforts to find their way through the labyrinth of emotional and cognitive dissonance that litters the health and healthcare landscape. As authors of *Bridges to Health and Healthcare,* we fervently hope that these obstacles will only detour but not ultimately deter individuals of compassion, conscience, and proven professional expertise on the road to efficacious healthcare.

STAKEHOLDER INTERVIEW LIST

1. Dr. Reginald Coopwood, President and CEO, The Regional Medical Center at Memphis

2. Stephen Reynolds, President and CEO, Baptist Healthcare Corporation

3. Gary Shorb, President and CEO, Methodist Healthcare

4. Anita Vaughn, Administrator and CEO, Baptist Memorial Hospital for Women

5. Jamie Patterson, Director of Operations, Department of Surgery, University of Tennessee Medical Group

6. Burt Waller, CEO, Christ Community Health Center

7. Dr. Peggy Veeser, Chair, Department of Nursing, Christian Brothers University

8. Yvonne Madlock, Director, Memphis and Shelby County Health Department

9. Elizabeth Bradshaw, Family Nurse Practitioner, Healthcare Consultant

'THE COMMUNITY CONVERSATION' ABOUT HEALTHCARE (THE OHIO STATE UNIVERSITY)

The Ohio State University Poverty Solutions Collaborative is incorporating aspects of the Bridges model into its multi-disciplinary process to reduce poverty and improve wellness for at-risk groups in central Ohio. The Bridges lens is one of many approaches being used by the collaborative.

The Multidimensional Nature of Poverty. The causes of poverty are many and varied. At the macro-economic and societal level, questions about investment in research and development, private property rights, access to capital, cultural values inconsistent with economic development, and the impact of politics, war, and civil war on the growth and persistence of poverty have all been raised. At a more micro level, questions about the relationship between individual entrepreneurial opportunities, access to clean water and health care, the role of education, the family structure, and the physical environment and poverty also have been discussed.

Clearly, poverty is not a phenomenon that can be understood through the lens of a single academic discipline. Even linking a few of these disciplines in an effort to understand the causes and consequences is inadequate to the task. What is required, instead, is a broad-based interdisciplinary approach to understanding the causes and consequences of poverty. Moreover, theoretical discussions about poverty will not realize their full potential until the implications of those discussions are put into practice in the field. After all, the study of poverty is not simply an intellectual exercise, but rather an essential step to help reduce its extent and effects.[79]

Under the direction of Louise Seipel, director of Community Engagement at the time (2010–12) and leader of the collaborative, several initiatives that engaged patients in poverty who were either uninsured or on Medicaid were developed and deemed successful in improving health and reducing poverty at some level for those involved. An early strategy used was called The Community Conversation; another ongoing program is the Community Health Workers Initiative.

The collaborative's Community Health Workers Initiative uses practically every one of the Bridges constructs. It is truly a multi-disciplinary approach, designed not only to improve health but develop workforce resources in a declining neighborhood. None of the Community Health Worker trainees have a college degree—and all were members of a specific neighborhood in Columbus, OH, with lower health indicators. One of the training steps in becoming a community health worker is participating in and completing a Getting Ahead in a Just-Gettin'-By World workgroup.

> This project seeks to create an entry path for paraprofessional training within a community-based health workforce model. The two primary aims are (1) to develop a workforce development program, directed at low-income residents that will prepare them to fulfill roles as community health workers, that encompasses social and supportive services necessary for job seekers to achieve job readiness and succeed long-term in the work force and (2) to develop a curriculum consistent with the standards for training of Community Health Workers (CHW) …
>
> **Getting Ahead in a Just-Gettin'-By World (GA) classes.** From April to June the 10 women selected attended 20 sessions of training. GA classes followed the Bridges Out of Poverty model, with adaptations to emphasize attitudes, behaviors, and skills necessary to succeed in a healthcare environment, according to Louise Seipel, Community Engagement director, and Kathy McPherson, GA facilitator. All 10

women completed training, a success rate unparalleled in our past experience in the community.

Enrollment in community health advocate (CHA) training program. Eight of the 10 graduates, as well as five additional applicants (involved in the Moms2B program) applied for the CHA program. Interviews were conducted at the end of June. Ten of 13 applicants were accepted, and nine enrolled.[80]

But before the Community Health Workers Initiative was fully developed, the collaborative wanted to engage people in poverty as "problem solvers" and create a forum where everyone's voice was heard. Community Engagement designed a series of "conversations" with graduates of the Getting Ahead in a Just-Gettin'-By World program, the co-investigative workgroup for individuals in poverty. Over a period of 15–20 weeks, the group had co-investigated every aspect of the view through the Bridges lens in order to determine personal and community strengths—and create a plan for personal and community sustainability. The graduates were mostly women, mostly in generational poverty, culturally diverse and living in Columbus. In the health forum settings, the graduates were joined by physicians and nurses in a "Community Conversation" about healthcare.

The Getting Ahead graduates had delved into the knowledge base of Bridges Out of Poverty over a period of 20 weeks and had co-investigated hidden rules of economic class, the resources model, the different mental models of economic class, the language and communication issues between/among economic class, and the power imbalances associated with economic class. Therefore, the GA graduates by and large trusted the GA facilitators who helped design The Community Conversation forums. Most people would agree with this statement: *If people I trust tell me I can trust the process, I tend to be willing to try it out.*

But in the actual conversation it turned out that years of perceived disrespect by multiple provider systems had morphed into a shared perception of rock-hard distrust and "group think"—with a retrenchment into "we/they." This development was met with almost philosophical resignation by the GA graduates. The experience may have been even more difficult for most of the healthcare professionals present. It's hard for many of us to read the summary of what happened. At some point you may be thinking, *Yes, yes, I know these problems; give me some solutions.*

When you reach that point, we ask you to simply continue. Continue to read what those who do not have much money or power said in these forums—without judgment or defensiveness. What then follows is analysis from the Bridges perspective, as well as some rather unique and creative solutions from the healthcare providers present.

But first, the way it was.

Getting Ahead graduates shared the following observations:	Healthcare providers responded to some of the concerns:
1. "HIPPA" is not the sister of Princess Kate. We get treated differently (this referred to interactions with clinical staff and providers), and we don't get the same medical treatment as other people. Everyone who deals with us knows what and who we are. They know we don't have insurance or that we're on Medicaid, so we don't get the same care as everybody else. *Interestingly enough, the graduates were not really satisfied with this assurance. The consensus was that there a lot ways of tell if someone is poor.*	The healthcare providers explained that this was not so—that the insurance issue was protected by the HIPAA legislation.
2. Triage is not a French designer. Because folks know we are poor, we are always last to get treated. This is done on purpose. This explanation made sense, but it was apparent that through the years the triage process and the long wait times in the ED had done some damage to relationships and trust. Triage was the reason, but this had been misunderstood by the graduates, and being last was often taken personally.	The healthcare providers explained that the emergency department (ED) had a triage process, and those who were more critical had to be seen first or immediately
3. Free means "not as good." We have to go to the free clinics. These doctors are not the good doctors. We get less experienced and less skilled doctors than people who have money and insurance.	

continued on next page

continued from previous page

Getting Ahead graduates shared the following observations:	Healthcare providers responded to some of the concerns:
4. If a question falls in the woods, does anyone hear it? Automatically you assume no one is going to listen. I don't think my doctor even cares about me. The graduates agreed with these statements. The answer was simple. The graduates said you could tell when someone doesn't care— because he/she doesn't listen to you. They don't believe what you're saying. Doctors and nurses are getting kickbacks from the drug companies, so they just give you drugs. A few graduates said that sometimes you would find someone who listened. But most had learned not to expect someone to listen and care. *None of the graduates knew the details about the managed-care system.*	A pediatrician who is very intentional about using the Bridges model was unnerved by this observation. She asked why the graduates thought this. Every doctor she knew cared and worked long hours for their patients. The healthcare providers explained why the doctor did not have much time to spend with each patient. They explained about the managed-care system and how many patients each doctor had to see every day—and how this is not really what doctors prefer, but it is the system in place.
5. Flying frequently does not always come with reward points. One woman told her story. She had an ED visit every month. She would have terrible stomach pains. She kept telling the ED doctors there is something really wrong. The woman said no one at the ED believed her. She suspected that because she came in so many times and was a poor woman, she was a "frequent flyer." Someone added, "Yes, they just think you want pain meds" and are making things up. They were dismissing what I was telling them! Finally, she had a life-threatening episode and got the right diagnosis. It took that. She said, "I almost died before I got the right answer."	

The healthcare providers' understandings and strategic responses:

- The providers at the table observed that their desire to be helpful was not connecting for the most part.

- Patients in poverty were mostly unaware of patient advocates. This needed to change.

- Phone numbers that patients could call to deal with bills were somehow being missed.

- The providers decided to look again at the language register in their paperwork and forms and to discuss how this information should be presented one on one with the patient.

- Providers determined that the phrase "Do you understand?" was completely missing the mark. Most of the time the patient would say yes, but really meant no. One provider suggested the practice of asking the patient to draw or explain what he/she understood.

    An OSU healthcare provider told the story of a patient interaction. After explaining the medication and dosage, the provider asked an older male patient, "How will you take it?" (The prescription was to be taken twice per day.) The patient responded, "Heck if I know; it doesn't say *when* to take it." The phrase "Tell me how you're going to take this" has now become the standard.

- One physician had a rather strange but insightful recommendation for her colleagues: *"Take the rollers off your chair!"* This idea came about from something one of the GA graduates had mentioned. "They always roll back when they're 'done,' even if you're still talking." The physician asked her colleagues, *"Were you aware that your patient knows that you're done with them before they're done with you?"*

    In the Bridges analysis, this is the power of the non-verbal, and individuals who use casual communication are *experts* at reading non-verbals.

From an interview with Louise Seipel—and conversations with Kathy McPherson and Dr. Jane Goleman, both of whom were part of these forums.

COMMUNITY CONVERSATIONS AND THE BRIDGES LENS: OF MUSICAL DISSONANCE, BOXING, AND OCEANS

First of all, it is important to remain nonjudgmental and to avoid being defensive when hearing ideas that seem so far from the perception of the system. It's much more meaningful if you have a lens—or a larger perspective. As a judge has said, "If I think the defendant is making no sense, I take off my achievement hat and put on my relationship hat." Then it makes more sense. If you hear it with "your relationship hat, not your achievement hat," it will more quickly translate into "I can see what to do."

Overlay a few elements of the Bridges model onto the conversations. The dialogue takes on a different focus. There is dissonance between two radically different driving forces. Dissonance is what happens when you play two adjacent keys at the same time on the piano. The sound waves bang against one another and make you want to say *Stop!* Think of those two musical notes boxing with one another. That's the physics of dissonance.

Did you notice the boxing match between the two main contenders, Relationship and Achievement? And did you take note of the hidden rules of power that play out?

The Achievement-driven contender has all the power and advantages, but this boxer also suffers the heavy burden of accountability for health outcomes. The Relationship contender is wiry and wily—and is full of surprises, resiliency, and sometimes unusual ways of solving problems that match a different set of resources.

If you don't see these hidden driving forces in your interactions and institutions, then Relationship and Achievement will just keep "duking it out" in dissonance—and nobody wins.

We look at best/great practices and replicate them. This is to be admired. If you're able to understand the underlying reasons *why* the practice works, so that you can innovate new models, this will bring you closer to so-called "blue ocean" thinking—seeing a much bigger picture and acting accordingly. "Red ocean" thinking is changing just a few aspects of a product for the same market. It is typically what most institutions do when they look at service redesign. Organizations seldom scrap nearly everything and start from scratch.

"Blue ocean" thinking is much more amazing. "Blue ocean" thinking is one description of how Bridges has evolved. It is an ongoing process of perceiving things from a larger view, creating and adapting Bridges ideas in original ways—thereby creating products (or service designs, community collaboratives, etc.) for markets no one knew existed. Welcome to the Bridges Community of Practice.

NOTE: To review how another organization, Ellis Medicine, has approached its community conversation—relationship building, personal engagements, and touches of "personal" moments as staff there have designed great practices to move patients from the emergency department to primary-care doctors—please see Chapter 5. Ellis is an excellent example of "what to do" once one sees the wider perspective offered by the Bridges lens.

SELECTED HEALTH AND HEALTHCARE RESEARCH

POVERTY TAXES THE BRAIN

In 2013 Emily Badger wrote:

> Poverty imposes such a massive cognitive load on the poor that they have little bandwidth ... a mental burden akin to losing 13 IQ points ... Coping not just with a shortfall of money, but also with a concurrent shortfall of cognitive resources.[81]

POVERTY AND DEATH

In 2011 Debra Watson wrote:

> A research team from Columbia University's Mailman School of Public Health in New York City has estimated that 875,000 deaths in the USA in 2000 could be attributed to a cluster of social factors bound up with poverty and income inequality ... According to U.S. government statistics, some 2.45 million Americans died in 2000. Thus the researcher's estimate means that social deprivation was responsible for some 36 percent of total U.S. deaths that year, a staggering total.[82]

Watson quotes Dr. Galea, chair of Mailman's Department of Epidemiology, as saying, "If you say that 291,000 deaths are due to poverty and income inequality, then those things matter too."[83]

CIGARETTE SMOKING

The Centers for Disease Control report:

> Tobacco use remains the single largest preventable cause of death and disease in the United States. Cigarette smoking kills more than 440,000 Americans each year, with an estimated 49,000 of these deaths from exposure to secondhand smoke. In addition, smoking-related illness in the United States costs $96 billion in medical costs and $97 billion in lost productivity each year.[84]

By income status, the report continues: "Below the poverty level, 29% smoke. At or above the poverty level, 17.9% smoke."[85]

Further, the CDC states:

> Secondhand smoke exposure is higher among persons with low incomes: 60.5% of persons living below the poverty level in the United States were exposed to secondhand smoke in 2007–2008, compared with 36.9% of persons living at or above the poverty level.[86]

OVERVIEW OF HEALTHCARE COSTS

Plunkett Research offers several cost-related facts, which include the following:

- Healthcare costs continue to rise rapidly in the United States and throughout the developed world. Total U.S. healthcare expenditures were estimated to be $2.8 trillion in 2012 and are projected to soar to $3.5 trillion annually by 2016.

- The healthcare market in the United States included the major categories of hospital care (about $884.7 billion), physician, dental, and clinical services ($735.4 billion), prescription drugs ($367.4 billion), along with nursing home and home health ($232.7 billion).

- Medicare, the U.S. federal government's healthcare program for Americans 65 years or older, provided coverage to 50.7 million seniors in 2012, with 2012 expenditures projected to be $590.8 billion, including premiums paid by beneficiaries.

As is widely known, Medicaid is the federal government's healthcare program for low-income and disabled persons (including children), as well as certain groups of seniors in nursing homes. While the federal government picks up a large percentage of this expense, states also absorb a significant share, which is a major burden on state budgets.[89]

Health and Economic Status

Age-Adjusted Percentage Distributions of Respondent-Assessed Health Status, by Selected Characteristics: United States, 2011

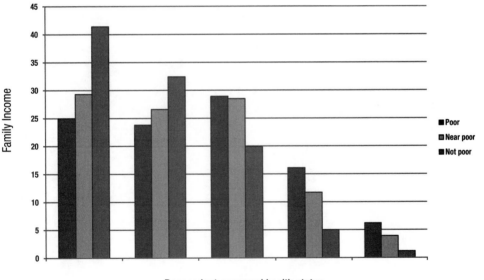

Source: Summary Health Statistics for the U.S. Population: National Health Interview Survey, 2011.

For a related Health and Economic Status chart, please see page 33.

COST DISPARITIES—BY NEIGHBORHOOD (INFORMAL RESEARCH)

Let's look at the cost of certain items in the drugstores throughout the community. For example, Kleenex. In this day and age, most people use a Kleenex tissue instead of a handkerchief. A professional colleague had a coupon for Kleenex at a certain national chain drugstore. In her middle-class neighborhood store of that chain, it was a certain price. Later that same day, while taking doing other errands, she had occasion to be in a store of that same national chain in a distressed neighborhood in the same town. The box of Kleenex cost considerably more. When she questioned the manager, she was told that was the price even though she had a receipt for the same brand, size, and color of tissue from the other store. Stores justify the markup to compensate, they say, for a higher level of shoplifting in those stores.

APPENDIX D

POVERTY RESEARCH CONTINUUM

POVERTY RESEARCH CONTINUUM

INDIVIDUAL BEHAVIORS AND CIRCUMSTANCES	COMMUNITY CONDITIONS
Definition: Research on the choices, behaviors, and circumstances of people in poverty	Definition: Research on resources and human and social capital in the city or county
Sample topics: ~ Racism ~ Discrimination by age, gender, disability, race, sexual identity ~ Bad loans ~ Credit-card debt ~ Lack of savings ~ Skill sets ~ Dropping out ~ Lack of education ~ Alcoholism ~ Disabilities ~ Job loss ~ Teen pregnancies ~ Early language experience ~ Child-rearing strategies ~ Bankruptcy due to health problems ~ Street crime ~ White-collar crime ~ Dependency ~ Work ethic ~ Lack of organizational skills ~ Lack of amenities	Sample topics: ~ Racism ~ Discrimination by age, gender, disability, race, sexual identity ~ Layoffs ~ Middle-class flight ~ Plant closings ~ Underfunded schools ~ Weak safety net ~ Criminalizing poverty ~ Employer insurance premiums rising in order to drop companies with record of poor health ~ Charity that leads to dependency ~ High rates of illness leading to high absenteeism and low productivity ~ Brain drain ~ City and regional planning ~ Mix of employment/wage opportunities ~ Loss of access to high-quality schools, childcare, and preschool ~ Downward pressure on wages

EXPLOITATION	POLITICAL/ECONOMIC STRUCTURES
Definition: Research on the impact of exploitation on individuals and communities	Definition: Research on political, economic, and social policies and systems at the organizational, city/county, state, national, and international levels
Sample topics: ~ Racism ~ Discrimination by age, gender, disability, race, sexual identity ~ Payday lenders ~ Lease/purchase outlets ~ Subprime mortgages ~ Sweatshops ~ Human trafficking ~ Employment and labor law violations ~ Wage and benefits theft ~ Some landlords ~ Sex trade ~ Internet scams ~ Drug trade ~ Poverty premium (the poor pay more for goods and services) ~ Day labor	Sample topics: ~ Racism ~ Discrimination by age, gender, disability, race, sexual identity ~ Financial oligarchy—the military, industrial, congressional complex ~ Return on political investment (ROPI) ~ Corporate lobbyists ~ Bursting "bubbles" ~ Free Trade Agreements ~ Recessions ~ Lack of wealth-creating mechanisms ~ Stagnant wages ~ Insecure pensions ~ Healthcare costs ~ Lack of insurance ~ De-industrialization ~ Globalization ~ Increased productivity ~ Minimum wage, living wage, self-sufficient wage ~ Globalization ~ Declining middle class ~ Decline in unions ~ Taxation patterns ~ Wealth-creating mechanisms

Source: *Getting Ahead in a Just-Gettin'-By World* by P. E. DeVol.

APPENDIX E

COMMUNITY ASSESSMENT TOOL

This Community Assessment tool is excerpted from *Getting Ahead in a Just-Gettin'-By World* by Philip DeVol.

1. COMMUNITY ASSESSMENT OF ECONOMIC CONDITIONS

INDICATORS	T	F	?
1. The percentage of people in poverty is going down.			
2. The percentage of people in or near poverty (200% of the Federal Poverty Guidelines) is going down.			
3. The free and reduced lunch rate in all schools is going down.			
4. Income disparity is decreasing.			
5. The number and value of business loans in low-income areas is growing.			
6. There's growing diversity in employment sectors, such as manufacturing, service, technology, knowledge, health, construction, tourism, etc.			
7. The number of people employed by locally owned businesses is growing.			
8. There's a mix of employment opportunities so more people can move up economically.			
9. The annual investment in the community's infrastructure is rising.			
10. The downtown vacancy rate is declining.			

Scoring: All "T" (True) answers are positive, and all "F" (False) answers are negative. Add up the "T" answers and divide by 2 to get the score. For example, if there were 8 "T" answers, divide 8 by 2 to get a score of 4. Circle the "4" in the bar below. Then turn to the page with the bar chart titled "Community Assessment Mental Model." Use a colored marker to fill in spaces 1 through 4 on the bar for this assessment.

1	2	3	4	5

2. COMMUNITY ASSESSMENT OF HOUSING CONDITIONS

INDICATORS	T	F	?
1. Rental units for low-income renters that are 30% of income is more available than in previous years.			
2. Percentage of households able to afford a median single-family house is rising.			
3. Utilization of homeless shelters is going down.			
4. Doubling up (people living together) is going down.			
5. The number of vacant and abandoned houses and other structures is going down.			
6. Segregated housing by economic class is going down.			
7. Housing cooperatives and mutual rental or home ownership (people not related to each other) are going up.			
8. Housing that is inadequate, overcrowded, or costs more than 30% of income is going down.			
9. Waiting time for subsidized housing is getting shorter.			
10. The number of homeless people is going down.			

Scoring: All "T" (True) answers are positive, and all "F" (False) answers are negative. Add up the "T" answers and divide by 2 to get the score. For example, if there were 8 "T" answers, divide 8 by 2 to get a score of 4. Circle the "4" in the bar below. Then turn to the page with the bar chart titled "Community Assessment Mental Model." Use a colored marker to fill in spaces 1 through 4 on the bar for this assessment.

1	2	3	4	5

3. COMMUNITY ASSESSMENT OF FINANCIAL/BANKING CONDITIONS

INDICATORS	T	F	?
1. Bank loans for small-business start-ups is going up.			
2. Community Reinvestment Act (CRA) scores for local banks are improving.			
3. Participation in the CRA plans of banks by people in poverty and near poverty is going up.			
4. More banks are providing typical and fair financial services to low-wage workers.			
5. More credit unions and banks are offering fair loans to low-wage workers.			
6. More financial literacy classes are available to people in poverty and near poverty.			
7. Micro loans are more available to low-income people.			
8. Percentage of disposable personal income that is being saved is rising.			
9. The dollars spent in the local economy (local businesses, local labor, and local resources) is growing.			
10. Per-capita debt is going down.			

Scoring: All "T" (True) answers are positive, and all "F" (False) answers are negative. Add up the "T" answers and divide by 2 to get the score. For example, if there were 8 "T" answers, divide 8 by 2 to get a score of 4. Circle the "4" in the bar below. Then turn to the page with the bar chart titled "Community Assessment Mental Model." Use a colored marker to fill in spaces 1 through 4 on the bar for this assessment.

1	2	3	4	5

4. COMMUNITY ASSESSMENT OF JOBS, WAGES, AND WEALTH-CREATING CONDITIONS

INDICATORS	T	F	?
1. Median household income is going up.			
2. Weekly average earnings are going up.			
3. Hours of labor required to meet basic needs is going down.			
4. The number of employee-owned businesses is on the rise.			
5. The ratio of CEO salary to front-line staff employee wages is going down.			
6. Employers are using fewer temporary and part-time employees.			
7. The availability of affordable, high-quality childcare is on the rise.			
8. Transportation to work and agencies is becoming more reliable and affordable.			
9. The community has a living-wage ordinance.			
10. The number of businesses using Bridges concepts is on the rise.			

Scoring: All "T" (True) answers are positive, and all "F" (False) answers are negative. Add up the "T" answers and divide by 2 to get the score. For example, if there were 8 "T" answers, divide 8 by 2 to get a score of 4. Circle the "4" in the bar below. Then turn to the page with the bar chart titled "Community Assessment Mental Model." Use a colored marker to fill in spaces 1 through 4 on the bar for this assessment.

1	2	3	4	5

5. COMMUNITY ASSESSMENT OF PROTECTION FROM PREDATORS CONDITIONS

INDICATORS	T	F	?
1. The number of payday lenders, cash-advance shops, and check-cashing outlets is going down.			
2. Alternatives to payday lenders, cash-advance shops, and check-cashing outlets are going up.			
3. Employers are developing low-interest loans and savings strategies for low-wage workers.			
4. Alternatives are being developed for buy-here/pay-here car dealers.			
5. The Better Business Bureau, Chamber of Commerce, and other business leaders are taking a stand against predatory businesses.			
6. The number of employers who "ask" employees to work "off the clock" without pay is declining.			
7. Minimum-wage violations are going down.			
8. Workers'-compensation violations are going down.			
9. Human trafficking is going down.			
10. Drug trafficking is going down.			

Scoring: All "T" (True) answers are positive, and all "F" (False) answers are negative. Add up the "T" answers and divide by 2 to get the score. For example, if there were 8 "T" answers, divide 8 by 2 to get a score of 4. Circle the "4" in the bar below. Then turn to the page with the bar chart titled "Community Assessment Mental Model." Use a colored marker to fill in spaces 1 through 4 on the bar for this assessment.

1	2	3	4	5

6. COMMUNITY ASSESSMENT OF EDUCATION CONDITIONS

INDICATORS	T	F	?
1. High-quality, affordable preschool opportunities are on the rise.			
2. The percentage of children enrolled in Early Head Start is going up.			
3. The graduation rate of high school students is on the rise.			
4. School "report cards" on standardized test scores is rising.			
5. The graduation rate of first-generation, low-income college students is going up.			
6. Apprenticeship and certificate programs that lead to well-paying jobs are on the rise.			
7. Worker skills are increasingly meeting the needs of the employers.			
8. The cost of a college education is declining.			
9. The digital divide (the gap between those with access to computers and the Internet and those without access) is narrowing.			
10. The number of community colleges, colleges, and universities using Bridges concepts is on the rise.			

Scoring: All "T" (True) answers are positive, and all "F" (False) answers are negative. Add up the "T" answers and divide by 2 to get the score. For example, if there were 8 "T" answers, divide 8 by 2 to get a score of 4. Circle the "4" in the bar below. Then turn to the page with the bar chart titled "Community Assessment Mental Model." Use a colored marker to fill in spaces 1 through 4 on the bar for this assessment.

1	2	3	4	5

7. COMMUNITY ASSESSMENT OF PUBLIC SECTOR CONDITIONS

INDICATORS	T	F	?
1. The tax base for maintaining high-quality police and fire services is secure.			
2. The tax base for maintaining high-quality schools and recreational facilities is secure.			
3. The tax base for public transportation, water, sewer, garbage collection, and street cleaning is secure.			
4. Public transportation is adequate to move people to and from the workplace, school, healthcare facilities, and grocery stores.			
5. Governmental services usually treat everyone in a respectful and timely manner.			
6. Agencies collaborate to serve clients more effectively and efficiently.			
7. Governmental and non-profit organizations are providing a safety net (financial support for the aged, disabled, young, unemployed et al.) and increasingly providing support for those who are making the transition out of poverty.			
8. The percentage of taxpayer satisfaction with services is going up.			
9. The percentage of people who trust local government is going up.			
10. The public sector is increasingly using Bridges concepts in programming and service delivery.			

Scoring: All "T" (True) answers are positive, and all "F" (False) answers are negative. Add up the "T" answers and divide by 2 to get the score. For example, if there were 8 "T" answers, divide 8 by 2 to get a score of 4. Circle the "4" in the bar below. Then turn to the page with the bar chart titled "Community Assessment Mental Model." Use a colored marker to fill in spaces 1 through 4 on the bar for this assessment.

1	2	3	4	5

8. COMMUNITY ASSESSMENT OF HEALTH CONDITIONS

INDICATORS	T	F	?
1. The number of uninsured community members is declining.			
2. The cost of healthcare is declining.			
3. High-quality food is accessible and affordable to all.			
4. Environmental safety is improving for everyone.			
5. Transportation and easy access to healthcare is improving.			
6. Neighborhood crime is going down.			
7. Mental health and addiction treatment is affordable and accessible.			
8. Preventive healthcare is on the rise for all.			
9. The overall fitness of community members is rising.			
10. Health disparities are on the decline.			

Scoring: All "T" (True) answers are positive, and all "F" (False) answers are negative. Add up the "T" answers and divide by 2 to get the score. For example, if there were 8 "T" answers, divide 8 by 2 to get a score of 4. Circle the "4" in the bar below. Then turn to the page with the bar chart titled "Community Assessment Mental Model." Use a colored marker to fill in spaces 1 through 4 on the bar for this assessment.

1	2	3	4	5

9. COMMUNITY ASSESSMENT OF LEADERSHIP CONDITIONS

INDICATORS	T	F	?
1. The leadership in each sector increasingly ensures that people from all classes and races are engaged in planning, program design, implementation, and evaluation of major initiatives.			
2. The leadership in each sector is increasingly intentional about helping people in poverty make the transition to a stable economic situation.			
3. The leadership increasingly creates a culture of mutual respect for people of all classes and races.			
4. The leadership is increasingly collaborative and less prone to operating in "silos."			
5. The leadership is increasingly able to work across political lines to serve the whole community.			
6. The leadership increasingly supports locally owned and small businesses with incentives and tax breaks.			
7. The leadership is increasingly representative of the population in terms of race, ethnicity, and class.			
8. Citizen participation in community projects is increasing.			
9. The community has a Bridges Steering Committee or a similar group by another name that coordinates the work on poverty based on the Bridges constructs.			
10. The leadership is increasing the application of Bridges concepts in its area of influence.			

Scoring: All "T" (True) answers are positive, and all "F" (False) answers are negative. Add up the "T" answers and divide by 2 to get the score. For example, if there were 8 "T" answers, divide 8 by 2 to get a score of 4. Circle the "4" in the bar below. Then turn to the page with the bar chart titled "Community Assessment Mental Model." Use a colored marker to fill in spaces 1 through 4 on the bar for this assessment.

1	2	3	4	5

COMMUNITY ASSESSMENT MENTAL MODEL
(place scores here)

	ECONOMIC	HOUSING	FINANCIAL	JOBS, WAGES	PREDATORS	EDUCATION	PUBLIC SERVICES	HEALTH	LEADERSHIP
5									
4									
3									
2									
1									

Source: *Getting Ahead in a Just-Gettin'-By World* by P. E. DeVol.

APPENDIX F

STABILITY SCALE

STABILITY SCALE INDICATORS

	Extremely Unstable
Time horizon	Can't see past today
Housing	I have no housing or crowded housing, and I spend more than 35% of my income on housing
Bills	Most are overdue
Emotional	I can sometimes choose and control my emotional responses; I sometimes behave in ways that are harmful to me or others
Income	Less than 50% of my income is from wages and/or child support
Employment	I work less than 40 hours per week
Wages	I have no regular wage
Stress	I am rarely able to control the important things in life
Physical and mental health	Problems often interfere with my work or school
Legal issues	Legal problems interfere with my work or school
Safety	Family members often aren't safe in my house or neighborhood
Destructive behaviors of others	Destructive behaviors of others have lots of influence on me
Behavior of children	My children are pretty much out of control and often interfere with my work or school
Transportation	The transportation I use is often unreliable
Bridging social capital	I communicate with almost no one outside of my closest circle of family and friends

Unstable	Fairly Stable
Can see two or three weeks into the future and make plans	Can see a month or two months into the future and make plans
I have uncertain housing or crowded housing, and I spend about 35% of income on housing	I have assured housing, and I spend 30% or less of my income on housing
Some are overdue	None are overdue
I almost always choose and control my emotional responses; I almost never behave in ways that are harmful to me or others	I am good at choosing and controlling my responses; I almost always engage in positive behaviors toward others
Fifty to 80% of my income is from wages and/or child support	More than 80% of my income is from wages and/or child support
I work two or more jobs for a total of 40 hours per week	I have been employed full time for more than a year
I earn minimum wage	I earn a living wage
I am sometimes able to control the important things in life	I am usually able to control the important things in life
Some problems interference with my work and school	Problems rarely interfere with my work or school
I've taken care of my major legal problems	I've never had significant legal issues
Family members are safe in my house and neighborhood much of the time	Family members are safe in my house and neighborhood almost all of the time
Destructive behaviors of others have some influence on me	Destructive behaviors of others have little influence on me
My children behave most of the time; care for them is generally sufficient	My children's behavior doesn't interfere with my work or school
The transportation I usually use is generally dependable	The transportation I usually use is almost always dependable
I communicate with a few people outside of my closest circle of family and friends	I communicate with a number of people outside of my closest circle of family and friends

Source: Adapted from *Bridges/Getting Ahead Outcomes Indicators Scales, Technical Manual* by William W. Swan.

COMMUNITY SUSTAINABILITY GRID
A Comprehensive Planning Tool for
Bridges Steering Committees

Community Sustainability Grid
A Comprehensive Planning Tool for Bridges Steering Committees

Name the Barrier:	Individual Behavior	Human and Social Capital in the Community	Exploitation	Political/Economic Structures
Individual Action				
Organizational Action				
Community Action				
Policy				

Address All Causes of Poverty

Source: *Bridges to Sustainable Communities* by P. E. DeVol.

LESSONS FROM THE STREET:
DELANCEY STREET

Is there enough institutional and community will to create the type of collective-efficacy opportunities seen with the Delancey Street Foundation in San Francisco?

According to the Delancey Street Foundation:

> Delancey Street is the country's leading residential self-help organization for former substance abusers, ex-convicts, homeless and others who have hit bottom. Started in 1971 with four people in a San Francisco apartment, Delancey Street has served many thousands of residents in five locations throughout the United States. Residents at Delancey Street range from teenagers to senior citizens, and include men and women and all races and ethnicities. The average resident has been a hard-core drug and alcohol abuser, has been in prison, is unskilled, functionally illiterate, and has a personal history of violence and generations of poverty.[87] *http://www.delanceystreetfoundation. org/wwa.php*

The foundation states that the description for raising funds for building the first house for

> residents like Abe Irizarry (then a "graduate" of every prison in California and Mexican Mafia gang member, now our vice president and *maître d'* of our restaurant), and Joanne Mancuso (then an addict and now a college instructor and a trainer for the judiciary in the federal court in computer programs), and Mike Boris (then a heroin addict, now a Certified Public Accountant), sold raffle tickets where the most coveted prize was the promise "not to move next door to you."[88] *http://www.delanceystreetfoundation.org/ourstory.php*

The foundation continues:

> More than 35 years later we remain true to our mission. We have been taking in as residents representatives of our society's most serious social problems and, by a process of each one helping another, with no professionals, no government funding, and at no charge to the clients, we have been solving these problems: generations of poverty, illiteracy, lack of job skills, hard core substance abuse, homelessness, crime, violence, teen pregnancy, and emotional and physical abuse. After an average of four years (a minimum stay of two years), our residents gain an academic education, three marketable skills, accountability and responsibility, dignity, decency, and integrity.[90] *http://www.delanceystreetfoundation.org/ourstory.php*

What are the resources offered by Delancey Street Foundation? How has it leveraged community relationships and resources? The foundation also is used as a model for the power of community and culture in the book *Change or Die* by Alan Deutschman. This work addresses the question of one's capacity to change when change matters most.[91]

The clients and patients served in our nation's healthcare institutions often find themselves at the crossroads of the need to change—when *not* changing can have a profound deleterious impact on their ability to move forward with dignity.

APPENDIX I

JUST FOR FUN:
Analysis of an Undesirable Outcome in the Healthcare Delivery System

Analyze an undesirable outcome in the healthcare delivery system; pick any of the following you may have experienced or observed in which more than one person was involved. Please check the items that applied to your situation (could be more than one).

In the undesirable outcome you're thinking of, the communication was:
___ Complete
___ Accurate
___ Misleading
___ Adequate
___ Timely
___ Honest
___ Delivered
___ Received
___ Congruent with facial expression and/or body language
___ Limited to only a few of the people involved
___ Shared with all appropriate people
___ Other (describe below—and also describe what went wrong and why)

_____

_____

_____

How might the outcome have been different if, in all the encounters, the communication was non-judgmental and characterized by mutual respect among all concerned?

_____

_____

_____

ENDNOTES

[1] "Preamble to the Constitution of the World Health Organization."

[2] S. H. Woolf & A. Laudan (Eds.), *U.S. Health in International Perspective.*

[3] "Social Determinants of Health in Poverty."

[4] "Diseases of Poverty"; "Preamble to the Constitution of the World Health Organization."

[5] E. Badger, "How Poverty Taxes the Brain."

[6] E. H. Friedman, *A failure of nerve,* pp. 139–143.

[7] Ibid.

[8] S. Greenspan & B. Benderly, *The Growth of the Mind and the Endangered Origins of Intelligence.*

[9] S. Covey, *7 Habits of Highly Effective People.*

[10] "Introduction to the Health Care Industry."

[11] "Key Facts About the Uninsured Population."

[12] Sandoval et al., "Factors That Influence Cancer Patients' Overall Perceptions of the Quality of Care," p. 272.

[13] L. Alrubaiee & F. Alkaa'ida, "The Mediating Effect of Patient Satisfaction in the Patients' Perceptions of Healthcare Quality—Patient Trust Relationship," p. 115.

[14] A. Bandura, "Self-Efficacy: Toward a Unifying Theory of Behavioral Change," "Self-Efficacy Mechanism in Human Agency," and *Self-Efficacy: The Exercise of Control.*

[15] Although we will use efficacy (self, neighborhood, collective) in the commonly accepted ways, we will narrow and change the way we use the term institutional efficacy. Research about institutional efficacy and its relationship to self-efficacy has typically been done in education. Critics of the applicability of institutional efficacy in social service models will use crime and the death penalty as examples. Studies show that the death penalty does not seem to deter certain crimes despite the ability of certain institutions to administer it.

[16] A. Bandura, "Self-Efficacy: Toward a Unifying Theory of Behavioral Change," p. 195.

[17] M. Wheatley, *Leadership and the New Science.*

[18] R. M. Sapolsky, *Why Zebras Don't Get Ulcers.*

[19] M. Marmot & R. G. Wilkinson, *Social Determinants of Health.*

[20] "Addressing Racial and Ethnic Disparities in Health Care."

[21] A. Bandura, "Self-Efficacy Mechanism in Human Agency," *Self-Efficacy: The Exercise of Control,* and *Social Foundations of Thought and Action.*

[22] E. Durkheim, *The Division of Labour in Society.*

[23] aha! Process, "Bridges Out of Poverty" [video].

[24] D. Shipler, *The Working Poor.*

[25] R. K. Payne, *A Framework for Understanding Poverty.*

[26] Ibid.

[27] Ibid.

[28] An exception is C. Harper, R. Marcus, & K. Moore, "Enduring Poverty and the Conditions of Childhood."

[29] J. Lave & E. Wenger, *Situated Learning.*

[30] S. Durlauf, "A Theory of Persistent Income Inequality," "Neighborhood Feedbacks, Endogenous Stratification, and Income Inequality"; G. Akerlof, "Social Distance and Social Decisions"; R. Benabou, "Workings of a City," "Equity and Efficiency in Human Capital Investment," "Heterogeneity, Stratification, and Growth"; C. Bicchieri, *The Grammar of Society*; K. A. S. Wickrama & S. Noh, "The Long Arm of Community"; P. Sharkey, "The Intergenerational Transmission of Context."

[31] C. Harper, R. Marcus, & K. Moore, "Enduring Poverty and the Conditions of Childhood"; T. Leventhal & J. Brooks-Gunn, "The Neighborhoods They Live in"; W. J. Wilson, *The Truly Disadvantaged.*

[32] W. J. Wilson, *The Truly Disadvantaged*; R. Stanton-Salazar & S. Dornbusch, "Social Capital and the Reproduction of Inequality"; M. P. Fernandez-Kelly, "Towanda's Triumph"; B. Fine, *Social Capital Versus Social Theory*; M. Gonzalez de la Rocha, *Private Adjustments*; D. Narayan et al., *Crying out for Change*; A. Lareau, "Social Class Differences in Family-School Relationships."

[33] D. Shipler, *The Working Poor*; G. J. Duncan & J. Brooks-Gunn, *Consequences of Growing up Poor*; W. J. Wilson, *The Truly Disadvantaged*.

[34] C. W. Mills, *The Power Elite*.

[35] M. Joos, *The Five Clocks*.

[36] B. Hart & T. R. Risley, *The Social World of Children* and *Meaningful Differences in the Everyday Experience of Young American Children*.

[37] Cf. A. G. Halberstadt, "Race, Socioeconomic Status, and Nonverbal Behavior"; L. C. Quay & R. L. Blaney, "Verbal Communication, Nonverbal Communication, and Private Speech in Lower and Middle Socioeconomic Status Preschool Children."

[38] "National CLAS Standards," "Notices."

[39] A. Bandura, "Self-Efficacy: Toward a Unifying Theory of Behavioral Change," p. 193.

[40] Ibid., pp. 127–128.

[41] "FSG."

[42] M. Kramer, *Better Outcomes, Lower Costs*.

[43] A. Bandura: *Self-Efficacy: The Exercise of Control,* p. 356.

[44] "CFDA Health Initiative."

[45] Ibid.

[46] "AHA NOVA Award Recipients."

[47] A. Bandura, *Self-Efficacy: The Exercise of Control,* p. 53.

[48] E. C. Rich, T. Lake, & C. S. Valenzano, "Paying Wisely," p. 9.

[49] A. Bandura: *Self-Efficacy: The Exercise of Control*.

[50] E. C. Rich, T. Lake, & C. S. Valenzano, "Paying Wisely," p. 9.

[51] L. Curtin, "Quantum Leadership."

[52] R. Rowe & M. Calnan, "Trust Relations in Health Care."

[53] D. L. Darling & G. Randel, "Leadership for Healthy Communities."

[54] P. E. DeVol, *Getting Ahead in a Just-Gettin'-By World* (pp. 167–177).

[55] N. M. Stephens, H. R. Markus, & S. A. Fryberg, "Social Class Disparities in Health and Education."

[56] Institute for Healthcare Improvement, "The IHI Triple Aim Initiative."

[57] A. Sommers, E. R. Boukus, & E. Carrier, "Dispelling Myths About Emergency Department Use."

[58] M. Marmot, *The Status Syndrome*.

[59] R. M. Sapolsky, *Why Zebras Don't Get Ulcers*.

[60] Ibid.

[61] D. Shipler, *The Working Poor*.

[62] R. M. Sapolsky, *Why Zebras Don't Get Ulcers*.

[63] Ibid.

[64] Ibid.

[65] Ibid.

[66] P. Dekker & E. M. Uslaner, *Social Capital and Participation in Everyday Life.*

[67] R. Inglehart, *Modernization and Postmodernization,* p. 188.

[68] R. Putnam, *Bowling Alone.*

[69] Ibid.

[70] Ibid.

[71] A. Bandura, *Self-Efficacy: The Exercise of Control,* pp. 367–368.

[72] L. Y. Shaw, Written statement to chair of board of directors of The Regional Medical Center of Memphis.

[73] J. Kania & M. Kramer, "Collective Impact."

[74] P. E. DeVol, *Getting Ahead in a Just-Gettin'-By World.*

[75] P. E. DeVol, *Bridges to Sustainable Communities.*

[76] R. M. Sapolsky, *Why Zebras Don't Get Ulcers,* p. 383.

[77] P. Starr, *The Social Transformation of American Medicine.*

[78] Patient Protection and Affordable Care Act of 2010.

[79] H. Goldstein et al., "The Ohio State University Poverty Solutions Collaborative."

[80] H. Goldstein, "Workforce and Curriculum Development for Community Health Workers in Weinland Park."

[81] E. Badger, "How Poverty Taxes the Brain."

[82] D. Watson, "The Dramatic Effect of Poverty on Death Rates in the U.S."

[83] Ibid.

[84] "Cigarette Smoking in the United States."

[85] Ibid.

[86] Ibid.

[87] "Introduction to the Health Care Industry."

[88] "Who We Are."

[89] "Our Story."

[90] Ibid.

[91] A. Deutschman, *Change or Die.*

BIBLIOGRAPHY

Addressing racial and ethnic disparities in health care. (2013, April). Agency for Healthcare Research and Quality. Retrieved from http://www.ahrq. gov/research/findings/factsheets/minority/disparit/index.html

AHA NOVA award recipients: 1994–2004. (2014). American Hospital Association. Retrieved from http://www.aha.org/about/awards/NOVA-past.shtm

aha! Process. (2011, February 11). Bridges out of poverty [video]. Retrieved from https://www.youtube.com/watch?v=fFwAm7HDSwU

Akerlof, G. (1997). Social distance and social decisions. *Econometrica, 65,* 1005–1028.

Alrubaiee, L., & Alkaa'ida, F. (2011). The mediating effect of patient satisfaction in the patients' perceptions of healthcare quality—patient trust relationship. *International Journal of Marketing Studies, 3*(1), 103–127.

Badger, E. (2013, August 29). How poverty taxes the brain. The Atlantic Cities. Retrieved from http://www.theatlanticcities.com/jobs-and-economy/2013/08/how-poverty-taxes-brain/6716/

Bandura, A. (1977). Self-efficacy: Toward a unifying theory of behavioral change. *Psychological Review, 84*(2), 191–215.

Bandura, A. (1982). Self-efficacy mechanism in human agency. *American Psychologist, 37*(2), 122–147.

Bandura, A. (1986). *Social foundations of thought and action: A social cognitive theory.* Englewood Cliffs, NJ: Prentice Hall.

Bandura, A. (1997). *Self-efficacy: The exercise of control.* New York, NY: W. H. Freeman.

Barr, V., Robinson, S., Marin-Link, B., Underhill, L., Dotts, A., & Ravensdale, D. (2003). The expanded chronic care model: An integration of concepts and strategies from population health promotion and the chronic care model. *Hospital Quarterly, 7*(1), 73–82.

Benabou, R. (1993). Workings of a city: Location, education and production. *Quarterly Journal of Economics, 108*(3), 619–652.

Benabou, R. (1996). Equity and efficiency in human capital investment: The local connection. *Review of Economic Studies, 62,* 237–264.

Benabou, R. (1996). Heterogeneity, stratification and growth: Macroeconomic effects of community structure. *American Economic Review, 86,* 584–609.

Bicchieri, C. (2006). *The grammar of society.* Cambridge, England: Cambridge University Press.

California Newsreel (Producer). (2008). Unnatural causes: Is inequality making us sick? [Motion picture]. United States of America, California Newsreel.

CFDA health initiative. (2014). CFDA. Retrieved from http://cfda.com/programs/cfda-health-initiative

Chapman, E. (2008). *Radical loving care: Building the healing hospital in America* [2nd ed.]. Nashville, TN: Baptist Healing Hospital Trust.

Cigarette smoking in the United States. (2013, March 27). Centers for Disease Control and Prevention. Retrieved from http://www.cdc.gov/tobacco/campaign/tips/resources/data/cigarette-smoking-in-united-states.html

Clark, R. C. (2008). *Building expertise: Cognitive methods for training and performance improvement* (3rd ed.). San Francisco, CA: Pfeiffer.

The cost of diabetes. (2013, October 21). American Diabetes Association. Retrieved from http://www.diabetes.org/advocacy/news-events/cost-of-diabetes.html

Covey, S. R. (1990). *The 7 habits of highly effective people.* New York, NY: Simon & Schuster.

Curtin, L. (2013). Quantum leadership: Upside down. *American Nurse Today, 8*(3), 56–57. Retrieved from http://www.americannursetoday.com/assets/0/434/436/440/10018/10020/10038/10078/26c21e38-b4d1-4528-a357-60170bf6902d.pdf

Darling, D. L., & Randel, G. (1996). Leadership for healthy communities: Characteristics of healthy communities [MF-2064, revised]. Kansas State University. Retrieved from http://www.ksre.ksu.edu/bookstore/pubs/MF2064.pdf

Dekker, P., & Uslaner, E. M. (2001). *Social capital and participation in everyday life.* New York, NY: Routledge.

Deutschman, A. (2007). *Change or die.* New York, NY: HarperCollins.

DeVol, P. E. (2006). *Getting ahead in a just-gettin'-by world: Building your resources for a better life* [1st ed.]. Highlands, TX: aha! Process.

DeVol, P. E. (2009). *Bridges to sustainable communities: A systemwide, cradle-to-grave approach to ending poverty in America* [rev. ed.]. Highlands, TX: aha! Process.

DeVol, P. E. (2013). *Getting ahead in a just-gettin'-by world: Building your resources for a better life* [3rd ed.]. Highlands, TX: aha Process.

DeVol, P. E., Payne, R. K., & Dreussi-Smith, T. (2011). *Bridges out of poverty workbook* [2nd ed.]. Highlands, TX: aha! Process

Diseases of poverty. (2013, December 19). Wikipedia. Retrieved from http://en.wikipedia.org/wiki/Diseases_of_poverty

Duncan, G. J., & Brooks-Gunn, J. (Eds.). (1997). *Consequences of growing up poor.* New York, NY: Russell Sage.

Durkheim. E. (1893, 1997). *The division of labour in society.* New York, NY: Free Press.

Durlauf, S. N. (1996). Neighborhood feedbacks, endogenous stratification, and income inequality. In W. Barnett, G. Gandolfo, & C. Hillinger (Eds.), *Dynamic disequilibrium modeling.* Cambridge, UK: Cambridge University Press.

Durlauf, S. N. (1996). A theory of persistent income inequality. *Journal of Economic Growth, 1,* 75–93.

Durlauf, S. N. (2000). A framework for the study of individual behavior and social interactions. Retrieved from http://www.irp.wisc.edu/publications/dps/pdfs/dp122001.pdf

Durlauf, S. N. (2000). The memberships theory of poverty: The role of group affiliations in determining socioeconomic outcomes. Paper presented at Understanding Poverty in America: Progress and Problems. Madison, WI. Retrieved from http://www.irp.wisc.edu/publications/dps/pdfs/dp122101.pdf

Ferguson, R. (2013). Putting the prime in primary care. *Roots.* Jewish Healthcare Foundation and Pittsburgh Regional Health Initiative. Retrieved from http://www.jhf.org/Resources/PaperPdfs/roots-putting-the-prime-in-primary-care.pdf

Fernandez-Kelly, M. P. (1994). Towanda's triumph: Social and cultural capital in the transition to adulthood in the urban ghetto. *International Journal of Urban and Regional Research, 18,* 88–111.

Fine, B. (2001). *Social capital versus social theory: Political economy and social science at the turn of the millennium.* London, England: Routledge.

Friedman, E. H. (2007). *A failure of nerve: Leadership in the age of the quick fix* [Kindle ed.]. New York, NY: Church.

FSG. (2014). Retrieved from http://www.fsg.org/

Goldstein, H. (n.d.). Workforce and curriculum development for community health workers in Weinland Park. Retrieved from https://hsldigital.osu.edu/sitetool/sites/odswpublic/documents/Goldsteinppt1.pdf

Goldstein, H., et al. (n.d.). The Ohio State University poverty solutions collaborative. Retrieved from http://research.osu.edu/files/2010/05/PovertyCenterProposal.pdf

Gonzalez de la Rocha, M. (2000). *Private adjustments: Household responses to the erosion of work.* New York, NY: UNDP-SEPED.

Greenspan, S. I., & Benderly, B. L. (1997). *The growth of the mind and the endangered origins of intelligence.* Reading, MA: Addison-Wesley.

Halberstadt, A. G. (1985). Race, socioeconomic status, and nonverbal behavior. In A. W. Siegman & S. Feldstein (Eds.), *Multichannel integrations of nonverbal behavior* (pp. 227–266). Hillsdale, NJ: Lawrence Erlbaum.

Hanleybrown, F., Kania, J., & Kramer, M. (2012, January 26). Channeling change: Making collective impact work. *Stanford Social Innovation Review.* Retrieved from http://www.ssireview.org/blog/entry/channeling_change_making_collective_impact_work

Harper, C., Marcus, R., & Moore, K. (2003). Enduring poverty and the conditions of childhood: Lifecourse and intergenerational poverty transmissions. *World Development, 31(3),* 535–554.

Hart, B., & Risley, T. R. (1995). *Meaningful differences in the everyday experience of young American children.* Baltimore, MD: Paul H. Brookes.

Hart, B., & Risley, T. R. (1999). *The social world of children: Learning to talk.* Baltimore, MD: Paul H. Brookes.

Inglehart, R. (1997). *Modernization and postmodernization: Cultural, economic, and political change in 43 societies.* Princeton, NJ: Princeton University Press.

Institute for Healthcare Improvement. (2014). The IHI triple aim initiative. Retrieved from http://www.ihi.org/Engage/Initiatives/TripleAim/Pages/default.aspx

Introduction to the health care industry: Health expenditures and services in the US, 2013. (2014). Plunkett Research. Retrieved from www.plunkettresearch.com/health-care-medical-market-research/industry-and-business-data

Joos, M. (1967). *The five clocks.* San Diego, CA: Harcourt, Brace, & World.

Kania, J., & Kramer, M. (2011, Winter). Collective impact. *Stanford Social Innovation Review.* Retrieved from http://www.ssireview.org/articles/entry/collective_impact

Key facts about the uninsured population. (2013, September 26). Kaiser Family Foundation. Retrieved from http://kff.org/uninsured/fact-sheet/key-facts-about-the-uninsured-population/

Kramer, M. R. (2012). Better outcomes, lower costs: How community-based funders can transform U.S. health care, a conversation with Atul Gawande. Retrieved from http://www.fsg.org/Portals/0/Uploads/Documents/PDF/Better_Outcomes_Lower_Costs.pdf?cpgn=WP%20DL%20-%20Better%20Outcomes

Lareau, A. (1987). Social class differences in family-school relationships: The importance of cultural capital. *Sociology of Education, 60,* 73–85.

Laura, R. S., & Chapman, A., with Hinchey, M. (2009). *The paradigm shift in health.* Lanham, MD: University Press of America.

Lave, J., & Wenger, E. (1991). *Situated learning: Legitimate peripheral participation.* New York, NY: Cambridge University Press.

Leventhal, T., & Brooks-Gunn, J. (2000). The neighborhoods they live in: The effects of neighborhood residence on child and adolescent outcomes. *Psychological Bulletin, 126*(2), 309–337.

Marmot, M. (2005). *The status syndrome: How social standing affects our health and longevity.* New York, NY: Henry Holt.

Marmot, M., & Wilkinson, R. G. (2005). *Social determinants of health* [2nd ed.]. New York, NY: Oxford University Press.

McLeroy, K. R., Steckler, A., & Bibeau, D. (Eds.). (1988). The social ecology of health promotion interventions. *Health Education Quarterly, 15*(4), 351–377.

Mills, C. W. (1956, 2000). *The power elite.* New York, NY: Oxford University Press.

Narayan, D., Chambers, R., Shah, M. K., & Petesch, P. (2000). *Crying out for change.* Washington, DC: World Bank.

National CLAS standards: Fact sheet. (n.d.). Retrieved from https://www.thinkculturalhealth.hhs.gov/pdfs/NationalCLASStandardsFactSheet.pdf

National Health Interview Survey. (2013, December 30). Retrieved from http://www.cdc.gov/nchs/nhis.htm

Notices. (2013). *Federal Register, 78*(185). Retrieved from http://www.gpo.gov/fdsys/pkg/FR-2013-09-24/pdf/2013-23164.pdf

Our story. (2007). Delancey Street Foundation. Retrieved from http://www.delanceystreetfoundation.org/ourstory.php

Patient Protection and Affordable Care Act of 2010, Pub. L. No. 111-148, 124 Stat. 119 (2010). Retrieved from http://www.gpo.gov/fdsys/pkg/PLAW-111publ148/pdf/PLAW-111publ148.pdf

Payne, C. (2013, March 6). Diabetes costs nation $245 billion annually, study says. Retrieved from http://www.usatoday.com/story/news/nation/2013/03/06/diabetes-care-cost/1965185/

Payne, R. K. (2013). *A framework for understanding poverty: A cognitive approach* [5th rev. ed.]. Highlands, TX: aha! Process.

Payne, R. K., DeVol, P. E., & Dreussi-Smith, T. (2011). *Bridges out of poverty: Strategies for professionals and communities* [5th ed.]. Highlands, TX: aha! Process.

Preamble to the constitution of the World Health Organization. (1948). New York, NY: International Health Conference.

Putnam, R. D. (2000). Bowling alone: *The collapse and revival of American community.* New York, NY: Simon & Schuster.

Quay, L. C., & Blaney, R. L. (1992). Verbal communication, nonverbal communication, and private speech in lower and middle socioeconomic status preschool children. *Journal of Genetic Psychology, 153*(2), 129–138.

Rich, E. C., Lake, T., & Valenzano, C. S. (2012). Paying wisely: Reforming incentives to promote evidence-based decisions at the point of care. Center on Health Care Effectiveness. Retrieved from http://www.mathematica-mpr.com/publications/PDFs/health/chce_poc_wp.pdf

Rowe, R., & Calnan, M. (2006). Trust relations in health care: The new agenda. *European Journal of Public Health,16*(1), 4–6.

Sandoval, G. A., Brown, A. D., Sullivan, T., & Green, E. (2006). Factors that influence cancer patients' overall perceptions of the quality of care. *International Journal for Quality Health Care, 18*(4), 266–274. doi:10.1093/intqhc/mzl014

Sapolsky, R. M. (2004). *Why zebras don't get ulcers.* New York, NY: Macmillan.

Sharkey, P. (2008). The intergenerational transmission of context. *American Journal of Sociology, 113*(4), 931–969. Retrieved from http://www.stanford.edu/group/scspi/_media/pdf/Reference%20Media/Sharkey_2008.pdf

Shaw, L. Y. (n.d.). Written statement to chair of board of directors of The Regional Medical Center of Memphis. Copy in possession of author.

Shipler, D. K. (2004). *The working poor: Invisible in America.* New York, NY: Random House.

Social determinants of health in poverty. (2013, December 30). Wikipedia. Retrieved from http://en.wikipedia.org/wiki/Social_determinants_of_health_in_poverty

Sommers, A., Boukus, E. R., & Carrier, E. (2012, July). Dispelling myths about emergency department use: Majority of Medicaid visits are for urgent or more serious symptoms. HSC Research Brief No. 23. Center for Studying Health System Change.

Stanton-Salazar, R., & Dornbusch, S. (1995). Social capital and the reproduction of inequality: Information networks among Mexican-origin high school students. *Sociology of Education, 68,* 116–135.

Starr, P. (1984). *The social transformation of American medicine.* New York, NY: Basic Books.

Stephens, N. M., Markus, H. R., & Fryberg, S. A. (2012). Social class disparities in health and education: Reducing inequality by applying a sociocultural self model of behavior. *Psychological Review, 119*(4), 18–19. doi:10.1037/a0029028

Swan, W. W. (2007, September). Bridges/Getting Ahead model fidelity scale and Bridges/Getting Ahead outcome indicators scale. Retrieved from http://www.ahaprocess.com/wp-content/uploads/2013/10/Bridges-Getting-Ahead-Technical-Manual.pdf

Valenti, K. (2013). The Schenectady Bridges project: Using the Bridges model to build a communitywide health coalition. In J. Reynolds et al. (Eds.), *From vision to action: Best practices to reduce the impact of poverty in communities, education, healthcare, and more* (pp. 61–69). Highlands, TX: aha! Process.

Watson, D. (2011, July 13). The dramatic effect of poverty on death rates in the U.S. World Socialist website. Retrieved from http://www.wsws.org/en/articles/2011/07/pove-j13.html

Wheatley, M. (1992). *Leadership and the new science.* San Francisco, CA: Berrett-Koehler.

Who we are. (2007). Delancey Street Foundation. Retrieved from http://www.delanceystreetfoundation.org/wwa.php

Wickrama, K. A. S., & Noh, S. (2009). The long arm of community: The influence of childhood community contexts across the early life course. *Journal of Youth and Adolescence, 39*(8), 894–910.

Wilson, W. J. (1987). *The truly disadvantaged: The inner city, the underclass, and public policy.* Chicago, IL: University of Chicago Press.

Wilson, W. J. (1996). *When work disappears: The world of the new urban poor.* New York, NY: Knopf.

Woolf, S. H., & Laudan, A. (Eds.). (2013). *U.S. health in international perspective: Shorter lives, poorer health.* Washington, DC: The National Academies Press.

INDEX

[NOTE: Page numbers in *italics* refer to figures, charts, and graphs.]

ABOUT THE AUTHORS

Dr. Ruby K. Payne, PhD, is founder of aha! Process and an author, speaker, publisher, and career educator. She is a leading expert on the mindsets of economic class and on crossing socioeconomic lines in education and work. Recognized internationally for her foundational book, *A Framework for Understanding Poverty,* now in its 5th revised edition (1996, 2013) which has sold more than 1,500,000 copies, Dr. Payne has helped students and adults of all economic backgrounds achieve academic, professional, and personal success.

Dr. Payne's expertise stems from more than 30 years of experience in public schools. Dr. Payne has traveled extensively and has presented her work throughout North America, and in Europe, Australia, China, and India.

Dr. Payne has written or co-authored more than a dozen books. Another publication is *Bridges Out of Poverty* (1999, revised 2009), co-authored with Philip E. DeVol and Terie Dreussi-Smith, which offers strategies for building sustainable communities. Her career-long goal for raising student achievement and overcoming economic class barriers has become a cornerstone for efforts toward school improvement by educational districts across the country. In 2013, Achievement for All: Keys to Educating Middle Grades Students in Poverty was published by AMLE (Association for Middle Level Education).

Sequels to her original *Framework* book include *School Improvement: 9 Systemic Processes to Raise Achievement* (2010), co-authored with Dr. Donna Magee; *Research-Based Strategies: Narrowing the Achievement Gap for Under-Resourced Students* (2009); *Under-Resourced Learners: 8 Strategies to Boost Student Achievement* (2008); *Crossing the Tracks for Love: What to Do When You and Your Partner Grew Up in Different Worlds* (2005); *Hidden Rules of Class at Work* (2002), co-authored with Don Krabill; *Living on a Tightrope: a Survival Handbook for Principals* (2001), co-authored with Dr. William Sommers; and *What Every Church Member Should Know About Poverty* (1999), co-authored with Bill Ehlig.

In 2011 two of her publications were recognized with awards: *Removing the Mask: How Identify and Develop Giftedness in Students from Poverty* received a Gold Medal from Independent Publishers for Education, and *Boys in Poverty: Understanding DropOut* (Solution Tree Press) received the Distinguished Achievement Award from Association of Educational Publishers for Professional Development. Both were co-authored with the late Dr. Paul Slocumb.

Payne received a bachelor's degree from Goshen College, Goshen, IN; master's degree in English literature from Western Michigan University, Kalamazoo, MI; and her doctorate in educational leadership and policy from Loyola University, Chicago, IL.

Terie Dreussi-Smith, MAEd, is an educator, trainer, consultant, and author who formerly worked as a public school teacher and adjunct faculty member for several colleges. In 1996 she was one of the first professionals to adapt Ruby Payne's *A Framework for Understanding Poverty* from K–12 education to community environments and social service settings. This helped Ms. Dreussi-Smith make the transition into her role as co-author of both *Bridges Out of Poverty* (1999) and *Bridges to Health and Healthcare* (2014). She is a full-time consultant for aha! Process Inc., presenting and consulting up to 100 days a year. She has worked with every sector and in every type of community in her scope of practice.

The practical know-how and approach Ms. Dreussi-Smith brings to this work originates from decades of diverse front-line and middle-management positions within behavioral health, community college systems, and K–12 education. Her many years working in community youth development and alcohol- and drug-abuse prevention have given her a broader perspective and an inclination toward innovation. Her years as supervisor of Prevention Services offered problem-solving opportunities to engineer and design leading-edge initiatives promoting health and wellness in communities and institutions. Most of these operated within the public health model. She now leads the national Bridges Into Health and Healthcare Community of Practice.

Beginning in 2009, Ms. Dreussi-Smith was approached by multiple healthcare providers and public health professionals as she adapted Bridges Out of Poverty to more closely align with health and healthcare. These conversations transferred her focus for Bridges Out of Poverty toward its implications for health systems and medical practice. She began presenting "Bridges Into Health" and worked closing with a number of healthcare providers and public health groups, which produced promising results using the Bridges lens. Today Ms. Dreussi-Smith continues her work in this area, as well as in developing new models for using Bridges Out of Poverty within every aspect and sector of the community.

As a consultant, Ms. Dreussi-Smith's presentations for aha! Process include *A Framework for Understanding Poverty*, *Bridges Out of Poverty Health*, *Bridges to Health and Healthcare*, *Getting Ahead in a Just-Gettin'-By World*, *Understanding and Engaging Under-Resourced College Students*, and *Hidden Rules of Class at Work*.

She received a bachelor of arts in music at Kent State University, Kent, OH, and a master of arts in education, College of Mt. St. Joseph, Cincinnati, OH.

Lucy Y. Shaw, MBA, is a senior-level executive with a master's degree in business administration. She has progressive leadership experience in both healthcare and banking. Ms. Shaw rose through the ranks from bedside nursing in one of the largest and most prestigious private hospitals in the world to the position of president and CEO at The Regional Medical Center of Memphis (The Med), a "safety net" hospital with four world-class centers of excellence. At the time of her leadership in the early to mid-1990s The Med was a 465-bed academic medical center with 2,600 employees and a $400 million budget. Ms. Shaw has been described as being "qualified to lead, motivate, and inspire by virtue of a strong record of success for her and those whose lives she has touched."

Ms. Shaw is well-known for her expertise in financing and managing the care of the underserved. Her skills and abilities in those areas brought her before the U.S. Senate Finance Committee on several occasions as president of the National Association of Public Hospitals. As an innovative leader she has spoken at international venues as well. She has graced the covers of magazines as a trailblazer in health and healthcare. Ms. Shaw has served as honorary consul to New Zealand and on university and bank boards of directors. She has published books and articles on health and management issues, personal, spiritual, and professional development. She currently writes a weekly newspaper column, "Living the Life I Love."